Style Manual for Biological Journals

(SECOND EDITION)

Prepared by the Committee on Form and Style of the Conference of Biological Editors

Published for the Conference of Biological Editors by the
AMERICAN INSTITUTE OF BIOLOGICAL SCIENCES
3900 Wisconsin Avenue NW, Washington, D.C. 20016

*Library of Congress
Catalog Card Number: 60-15133*

First Edition 1960
Reprinted 1961
Second Edition 1964
Reprinted 1966
Reprinted 1969
Reprinted 1970

Correct citation:
Conference of Biological Editors, Committee on Form and Style. 1964. Style manual for biological journals. Second edition. American Institute of Biological Sciences, Washington, D. C.

ALL ORDERS SHOULD BE ADDRESSED TO:
AMERICAN INSTITUTE OF BIOLOGICAL SCIENCES
3900 WISCONSIN AVENUE NW, WASHINGTON, D. C. 20016

Preface

(TO THE SECOND EDITION)

Several manuals and books containing suggestions for the preparation of manuscripts existed when a style manual was first considered by the Conference of Biological Editors. Hence, biologists were concerned whether this would be just one more manual, even after 80 journals had adopted it in whole or in part before final publication. But during the past 3 years the demand for this manual has exceeded expectations, and a new edition seems desirable.

Many suggestions have been sent to the Committee on Form and Style for consideration in preparing a new edition. The Committee has reviewed them all and has incorporated the most useful ones in this edition. The members of the Committee thank everyone who has given time and thought to the improvement of this manual.

The most extensive changes in this edition appear in the abbreviations of words used in literature citations. These are in keeping with the policy of accepting recognized standards where such exist. A Subcommittee on Periodical Title Abbreviations of the American Standards Association (Sectional Committee Z39 Library Work and Documentation) has a Proposed American Standard for Periodical Title Abbreviations. The Committee on Form and Style has voted to recommend adoption of the proposals for biological journals.

The Committee will welcome comments from users of this revised manual. Send your suggestions to:

Conference of Biological Editors, Committee on Form and Style
American Institute of Biological Sciences
2000 P Street NW, Washington, D.C. 20036

Committee on Form and Style
J. R. Porter, *Chairman*
James S. Ayars   Robert V. Ormes
Harold Cummins   A. J. Riker
*Graham DuShane   William C. Steere
Richard H. Manville   H. B. Vickery

* Deceased 18 July 1963

Note to the Second Printing of the Second Edition: This printing of the Second Edition does not differ substantially from the first. Errors called to the attention of the Committee on Form and Style have been corrected, but no changes involving style have been made. All suggested changes received by the Committee are on file and will be considered for inclusion in the Third Edition. Additional suggestions for change should be addressed as follows:

Council of Biology Editors, Inc.
(Successor to Conference of Biological Editors)
Committee on Form and Style
American Institute of Biological Sciences
3900 Wisconsin Avenue NW
Washington, D. C. 20016

Preface

(TO THE FIRST EDITION)

This style manual is designed for research workers preparing manuscripts for publication in biological journals, and for students and other prospective authors. Style is interpreted broadly to mean forms of expression in scholarly writing, and the general technical requirements of journals, such as details for typing manuscripts, standard abbreviations, and citation of references.

Not all fields can be covered completely, but it is our hope that this manual will be accepted, at least in part, by most biological disciplines. The instructions and recommendations represent good usage and practice; if followed, they will establish high standards in biological publication.

Many journals are using this manual in whole or in part. The following adopted it in advance of publication:

Agronomy Journal
American Biology Teacher
American Journal of Botany
American Journal of Human Genetics, The
American Journal of Physiology

American Midland Naturalist, The
American Potato Journal
Annals of the Entomological Society of America
Applied Microbiology

Archives of Oral Biology
Arthritis and Rheumatism
Association of Southeastern Biologists
  Bulletin, The
Auk, The. A Quarterly Journal of
  Ornithology

Bacteriological Reviews
Biological Abstracts
Biologist, The
BioScience
Blood
Brittonia
Bryologist, The
Bulletin of the Entomological Society of
  America
Bulletin of the Florida State Museum
Bulletin of the Research Council of Israel.
  Section B, Zoology. Section D, Botany.
  Section E, Experimental Medicine
Bulletin of the Torrey Botanical Club

Canadian Field-Naturalist, The
Catalogue of American Amphibians and
  Reptiles
Circulation Research
Copeia

Ecological Monographs
Ecology
Economic Botany
Entomological News

Federation Proceedings
Forest Science

Green Thumb, The
Growth. A Journal for Studies of Develop-
  ment and Increase

Human Biology

Illinois Natural History Survey Biological
  Notes
Illinois Natural History Survey Bulletin
Illinois Natural History Survey Circular
Illinois Natural History Survey
  Manual
International Bulletin of Bacteriological
  Nomenclature and Taxonomy

Iowa State Journal of Science
Iowa, State University of, Studies in
  Natural History

Journal of Applied Physiology
Journal of Bacteriology
Journal of Biological Chemistry
Journal of Dairy Science
Journal of Economic Entomology
Journal of General and Applied Micro-
  biology, The (Tokyo)
Journal of Histochemistry and Cyto-
  chemistry, The
Journal of Immunology
Journal of Insect Pathology
Journal of Lipid Research
Journal of Mammalogy
Journal of Parasitology, The
Journal of Protozoology, The
Journal of the National Cancer Institute
Journal of Wildlife Management

Limnology and Oceanography
Lloydia, A Quarterly Journal of Biological
  Science

Metabolism
Mycologia

Ohio Journal of Science, The

Papers of the Michigan Academy of Science,
  Arts, and Letters
Physiological Reviews
Physiologist, The
Phytopathology
Plant Physiology
Proceedings of the Academy of Natural
  Sciences, Philadelphia
Proceedings of the Biological Society of
  Washington
Progress in Cardiovascular Diseases
Public Health Reports (U.S.)

Quarterly Journal of the Florida Academy
  of Sciences, The
Quarterly Review of Biology, The

Science

Soil Science Society of America
Proceedings
Systematic Zoology

Transactions of the American
Microscopical Society

Toxicon

Weeds
Wildlife Disease
Wildlife Review
Wilson Bulletin, The

The Committee on Form and Style of the Conference of Biological Editors has been responsible for preparing this manual. But without the cooperation, suggestions, and talents of many people the project would have been impossible. Drafts of the manual have been read by approximately 100 editors and publishers. W. O. Nagel, Technical Writer for the Missouri Conservation Commission, has served as a valuable technical consultant to the Committee. Past and present officers (Bentley Glass, Milton O. Lee, Fred R. Cagle, Wallace O. Fenn, James G. Dickson, and Hiden T. Cox) of the Conference of Biological Editors and the American Institute of Biological Sciences have helped in many ways. The National Science Foundation provided generous financial support. To these people and agencies, the Committee expresses its thanks and appreciation.

Citation of the manual as a reference should be as follows:

Conference of Biological Editors, Committee on Form and Style. 1960. Style manual for biological journals. American Institute of Biological Sciences, Washington. 92 p.

If this manual is to be useful, it must be kept up to date by frequent revision. Comments by users will be helpful. Address suggestions to Conference of Biological Editors, Committee on Form and Style, American Institute of Biological Sciences, 2000 P Street NW, Washington 6, D.C.

Committee on Form and Style
J. R. Porter, *Chairman*
Sheridan Baker
George B. Cummins
Harold Cummins
Graham DuShane

Richard H. Manville
Robert V. Ormes
A. J. Riker
William C. Steere
H. B. Vickery

Contents

1. Writing

General Principles Learn to write effectively. To referees and editors, and especially to readers, you owe accurate, clear, and concise writing. You also owe brevity to the publishing journal, since costs are high and competition for space is keen. Prepare your manuscript carefully and in standard format; use double spacing between lines, proper headings, and ample margins.

Lead the reader from a clear statement of your subject or purpose, through the procedures and data, on to conclusions. Think of your paper as having these main parts: introduction, materials and methods, results, discussion, literature cited, and abstract.

The introduction should open with a succinct statement of the subject, should orient the report in its field, and should explain the purpose.

Describe your materials and methods in sufficient detail so that another worker can repeat the procedures exactly.

In the section dealing with results, arrange the data in unified and coherent sequence, so that the report develops clearly and logically. Use only such tables, photographs, drawings, or charts as are necessary to clarify and document the text. Avoid extensive discussion.

The discussion section should relate the new findings to previous results and include logical deductions.

The abstract should summarize only the major results and conclusions.

Concise Language Use words with precision, clarity, and economy. Every sentence should be exact and as simple as possible. Economy and accuracy require using the straightforward English sentence with all parts showing: subject, verb, and object.

Follow a consistent pattern of tenses. Record observations and experiments in the past tense; use the present tense for generalizations and references to stable conditions.

Use the passive voice only when necessary for emphasis; it requires extra words and may not convey the intended meaning. Compare *Fungi produce antibiotics* with *Antibiotics are produced by fungi.* The passive here requires two more words, and 25% more space. Worse, its idle words are not merely superfluous; they obscure the words that do the work. *It was found to have had* is simply, in the active voice, *It had.*

Biological publication now costs almost 6 cents a word. But more than money is at stake. Economy of communication and reading time is the major concern. Economy of words also yields clarity. *I found* costs less than half as much as *it was discovered,* and it identifies the discoverer immediately. When *experiments were conducted,* the reader cannot tell whether you or your predecessors conducted them. If you use *I* or *we* (*we* for two or more writers, never as a substitute for *I*), you easily avoid the passive voice, at least in that one sentence. *I* may embarrass *the writer,* but it takes less than one-tenth the space. It is also clearer, for *the writer* is often ambiguous:

These analyses, according to Smith, were inconclusive. Though the samples analyzed were collected from localities unknown to the writer . . .

When you finish your first draft, study each sentence to see whether you can shorten or even omit it. Delete unnecessary words to increase clarity and accuracy. You may even enjoy this word game, and the prize is increased professional competence. *It is interesting to note that,* for instance, does no real work and makes dull reading. Change every *It was discovered that* to *I found;* change every *It was reported by Smith* to *Smith reported.* Be alert for *by* as the danger sign of the passive voice.

Which and *of* may be signs of wordiness. The words *very, much, more,* and *quite* have a place, but are frequently misused as super-superlatives. If a word expresses an absolute quality or condition, the comparative has no place. For example, something can be *complete, immediate, adequate, sterile,* or *universal.* Although it cannot be *very complete* or *quite adequate,* it can be *nearly complete* or *adequate to a situation.*

Avoid misleading phrases and jargon of your field (this does not mean technical terms). The term *schizophrenic blood* is a misleading substitute for *the blood of schizophrenic patients.*

Use simple words; they save space. Compare *But* (no comma) with *However* (and comma) as a sentence beginning; *But* saves over 60%. Writing can be too compact, but wordiness is the common fault and should be corrected before you test for excessive terseness.

The final test (to be applied constantly, sentence by sentence) is whether the meaning is simply and clearly stated. Rewrite your paper several times. Then submit it to patient, critical colleagues; they may find flaws you have overlooked.

Unnecessary repetition, extraneous details, and loose phrases can obscure even simple ideas. Here is a paragraph (cited by Riker, 1946) from a paper submitted for publication:

> The multiplication of resistant white pine trees by means of making grafts has been already demonstrated as a feasible possibility. On an experimental basis, as was explained earlier, over 1,000 grafts have been made and grown successfully during these studies in both green house [greenhouse] and field conditions. Yet a grafted tree has been found relatively expensive because of the necessity, according to present technique, of using green house space in the winter time and cold frames in the spring. Counting scions, stock, pots, labor, *et cetera,* each graft is estimated to cost about 12 cents. This cost might be reduced somewhat if further research will be done to further improve the methods employed. It might also be reduced by putting [sic] this operation on the basis of a large scale commercial production. Even at this relatively high figure grafting may now be done as a practical possibility due to the high price paid for certain types of ornimental [sic] planting. But the most promising means that has [sic] appeared of reducing the cost of propagating rust resistant white pine trees is through the rooting of cuttings.

Much of this can be weeded out by careful rewriting:

> Propagation of rust-resistant white pine by grafting is feasible, but grafted trees are too expensive (about 12 cents each), except for certain ornamental plantings. Improved technique and large-scale commercial production may reduce the cost of grafted trees, but the use of rooted cuttings seems more promising.

Hedging The definition of the intransitive verb *to hedge* is "to arrange a way to escape or retreat." Even scientific writers sometimes wish to hedge or convey some degree of doubt in the statements they make. Absolute certainty is an ideal seldom attained, but the nearest approach to it is dignified as a *law of nature.* The law of gravitation, the Mendelian laws, and innumerable equations in physics and mathematics illustrate this. At a somewhat lower level of certainty are *theories,* for these are subject to revision to a greater or lesser degree as knowledge increases. A *theory* is a general principle offered to explain a phenomenon, a verified hypothesis widely applicable, and if you write this word make sure that you use it in this sense and no other. An *hypothesis* is a provisional conjecture, a proposition assumed for argument or test, or, from its Greek derivation, a foundation or supposition leading to investigation or study. When sufficiently verified and of wide application it leads to theory, as Darwin's hypothesis of survival of the fittest led him to the theory of evolution. All research more rewarding than the mere counting and recording of events is founded upon an hypothesis.

At a still lower level of certainty are such words and terms as *view, supposition, idea, notion, consideration, speculation, conjecture, surmise, thought,* and even *guess,* such qualifications as *probably, possibly, apparently,* and such verbs as *indicate, suggest, appears to be, seems to be, may,* and especially its past tense *might.* When it is necessary to hedge, and unfortunately this may happen frequently, select the precise word that describes the situation. But do not overdo it; the sentence "The fact that the active enzyme system is found only in the chlorophyllous plant *may be suggestive of a possible* function in the photosynthetic reactions" contains what may be regarded as a third order or triple-barrelled hedge.

Word Usage Use words in their exact meaning, referring when necessary to a dictionary. If there are synonyms, select the one that best conveys your meaning. Consider, for example, whether two objects are *joined, connected, united, linked, annexed, coupled, associated,* or *attached;* they may even *inosculate* or *anastomose,* or perhaps they merely *communicate* or *interdigitate.* You may *demonstrate, reveal,* or even *show the position of* spots on a paper chromatogram by spraying with a reagent, but this procedure does not *visualize* the spots. To visualize is to picture mentally; it happens in the mind, not on paper.

Make sure that you use technical terms precisely. If you used spinach *leaves* or the *flower buds* of cauliflower or carrot *roots,* say so at least once; if *serum,* specify the animal; if *leaves* of tea or tobacco, tell whether they are *green* leaves or the *prepared* leaves of commerce. The reader can only guess if you do not make such important details clear.

Remember that a verb must agree with its subject in number, either singular or plural. For example, *data, grams,* and *media* are plural words and need plural verbs. In the sentence, "The tissue was weighed and several samples cut from it," the author did not realize that the second subject should have a plural verb.

THE NOUN-HABIT   Although some nouns can be properly used as modifiers (*horse* fly, *tree* house, *midyear* examination), avoid using them in confusing clusters ("a new *type motor skills college performance* test"; "a *percentage transmission* recording *ultraviolet light absorption* meter"; "when the pooled within *photograph* partial *regression equation* was calculated").

Avoid habitual use of nouns or relative pronouns where use of adjectives, adverbs, or participles makes for greater conciseness. Write
1) "The rod, *which is 3 m long,*" "the rod, *3 m long,*" or "the *3-m rod,*" rather than "the rod, *which has a length of 3 m.*"
2) "The research *is important* to biologists," or "the research, *very important* to biologists," instead of "the research is *of great importance* to biologists."
3) "A technique *that was widely used* 5 years ago" or "a technique *widely used* 5 years ago," instead of "a technique *that was in wide use* 5 years ago."
4) "A process for *avoiding waste*" instead of "a process for *the avoidance of waste.*"

Complex noun constructions, the passive voice, and inaccurate wording may combine to obscure meaning and waste space.

OF AND WHICH   Here is a passage suffering from the *of and which* disease (cited by Baker, 1956):

Many biological journals, especially those *which* regularly publish new scientific names, now state in each issue the exact date *of* publication *of* the preceding issue. In dealing with journals *which* do not follow this practice, or with volumes *which* are issued individually, the biologist often needs to resort to indexes... in order to determine the actual date *of* publication *of* a particular name.

Eliminate *of*'s and the nouns they bring in, change *which*-phrases into participles, and a noun to a verb, and you have:

Many biological journals, especially those regularly *publishing* new scientific names, now give the exact date of the preceding issue. For journals not *adhering* to this practice, and in some books, the biologist must turn to indexes ... *to date* the publication of a particular name.

Wisely used, a participle saves at least one word (the linking *which*) and may ease a passage built entirely of static *of* or *which* segments.

DANGLING PARTICIPLES
AND INFINITIVES

Dangling or "hitchhiking" participles and infinitives are astonishingly common in science writing. They occur most frequently in sentences written in the passive voice, for such sentences often do not name the agent of the action suggested by the participle or infinitive. Hence the action is attributed, sometimes with ludicrous implications, to an agent that cannot perform the action:

Judging by present standards, these *trees* are ....
Looking through the microscope, the *cells* could be ....
Nitrogen was determined, using the *Kjeldahl method* ....
To determine stomatal closure ..., detached *leaves* were placed ....

The simplest remedy for the first example is to change the present to the past participle, *judging* to *judged,* and bring the subject forward in the sentence: "These trees, judged by present standards, are ...." The next two examples profit from dropping the participle altogether: "Under the microscope, cells could be ..."; "Nitrogen was determined by the Kjeldahl method ...." In the last example change the main clause to the active voice: "To determine stomatal closure ... , I placed ...."

A common renegade among participles is *following* in the sense of *after,* as: *following* the talk he visited the laboratory. Present participles, functioning as simple adjectives, often adhere to the wrong noun. What does "the enzyme oxidizing malate" mean: "malate that oxidizes the enzyme" or "the enzyme that oxidizes malate"? The second meaning is correct. Even if understood as the author intended, the present participle here erroneously implies a continuous process in the present. Use a cautious *which* or, preferably, *that*: "the enzyme that oxidizes malate." Good usage favors *that* for defining clauses and *which* for descriptive clauses (those set off by commas). If a participle dangles, or clings the wrong way, a *that* may save you from the *whiches*.

CONFUSING PAIRS   Several pairs of words of somewhat similar meaning confuse many begin-
ners and even some experienced writers in science. *Affect* is a verb and
means to influence or act upon; *effect* as a noun is the result of the influence, but as a verb it means to produce, do, make, accomplish, or bring
about. In the sentence, "To determine stomatal closure in the wilted leaves
and how this was *effected* by treatment, detached leaves were placed in water
. . . ," it is difficult to tell what the author meant. If he meant *effect,* it is
implied that he brought about closure of the stomata by his treatment.
But if he really meant *affect,* he was simply proposing to inquire into the
cause of the observed event. In the one case he controlled a biological
phenomenon; in the other, he did not. The situations are quite different.

Accuracy is an estimate of the degree to which a statement or quantitative result approaches the truth; *precision* is an estimate of the exactness
with which a given procedure can be repeated. A color-blind person can
sort beads of different colors into groups of the same color with, presumably, high *precision,* but his result will be grossly *inaccurate* because he will
put red beads with gray ones. *Accuracy* is freedom from error, *precision* is
freedom from variation, and one does not always imply the other. Unfortunately, many dictionaries fail to make entirely clear the distinction between
these words in scientific usage.

To *enable* is to provide power or competency to be or do something. To
permit is to allow or authorize. The sentence "Knowledge of specific
activities as functions of time *enables* the calculation of velocity constants"
is incomplete unless the phrase "to be made" is added. But if *permits* is sub-
stituted for *enables,* the sentence becomes complete.

Distinguish between *varying* and *various.* The sentence "Light intensity
was controlled by cheesecloth shades of *varying* thickness" is inaccurate
since no shade changed its thickness during the experiment. The shades
were of *various* thicknesses.

To *assure* is to confirm or make certain. To *insure* is to guarantee or
secure against risk. One *insures* himself against error by taking certain
precautions with the methods used. He may then *assure* himself or others
of their accuracy.

To *infer* is to derive by reasoning; to *imply* is to involve or intimate a
meaning not expressed. A result may be *fateful* but is not necessarily either
fated or *fatal.* Other pairs sometimes encountered in scientific writing are
alternate and *alternative, compose* and *comprise, connote* and *denote,*
predicate and *predict, purport* and *purpose, proportion* and *portion, re-*

course and *resort, reversal* and *reversion. Species* is both singular and plural; *specie* means gold or silver coin and its use as the singular of *species* is illiterate. When in doubt or when uncertain, do not *flout* the dictionary; this is as unwise as it is to *flaunt* your knowledge.

WHILE, ALTHOUGH, AND SINCE
Do not begin a sentence intended to express a contrast with *while*; use *although* or *though* or, infrequently, *since. While* implies a sense of time, i.e., during the time that. *Although* and *though* mean granting that, in spite of, or notwithstanding. *Since* often implies a sense of time, but it also means in view of, or merely because.

SIMILE AND METAPHOR
Be sure your figures of speech are appropriate and consistent. A simile explicitly compares one thing (relation or action) to something of a different kind, class, or quality; the comparison is usually illustrative and introduced by *like, as, as if,* or *as when.* "The water is as blue as the sky." Do not mix the figures, as: "Your contribution will seem like a drop in the bucket of this great bundle of red tape." In metaphor, a word or phrase denotes immediately one kind of object or idea in place of another by suggesting a likeness or analogy between them: "The professor *punctured* my excuses with a question"; "A mad bull is a *demon of energy.*" Use metaphors sparingly and avoid mixed comparisons that lead to absurdity:

Already there are indications that astronautics is upsetting the familiar applecart in which for generations we have piled our most precious ideas and rationalizations which protect and comfort us in the midst of the sea of ignorance which is our true cosmic environment. What is more important is that the impact of astronautics is only beginning to be felt and that this influence will rapidly mushroom to almost infinite proportions.

Jargon
Jargon is the slang or shorthand of spoken or written technical language; in the interests of clarity and good taste avoid it in formal reports. *Supernate* is chemical laboratory jargon for *supernatant fluid.* Scientists often manufacture technical nouns by adding *ate,* a suffix indicating the result of a process, to a stem implying action. Many of these, such as *exudate, eluate,* and *diffusate* are today in good usage; others (*photosynthate* and *homogenate*) are on the borderline. But *leachate,* referring to an extract from soil, is jargon. *Filtrate* is clearly that which has been filtered, but writers occasionally mistakenly apply it to the residue on the filter, for both, in a sense, have been filtered. Such inventions as *dialysate* and *centrifugate* compound the confusion, and neologisms such as *grindate* ("The glands

were . . . ground in a small, all-glass homogenizer and the *grindate* [was] centrifuged . . ."), *shockate, pressate, washate,* and *sonicate* are hardly understandable. The author of the last of these intended it as a designation for material that had been disintegrated by ultrasonic vibration, and *washate* was presumably meant to be wash fluid; *shockate* and *pressate* merely puzzle the reader. Although many widely used verbs end in *ate* (e.g., *propagate, fractionate, proliferate*), beware of constructing new ones as in "The suspension was centrifuged to *sedimate* the mitochondria."

Thoughtlessly used prefixes and suffixes also produce jargon. *Preincubate, unincubate, destabilize, prewarmed, prewet* (for moistened) , *pre-test phase, pre-steady state* are examples of such carelessness.

Innumerable acceptable verbs are constructed by attaching the suffix *ize* to a noun, meaning to make into or cause to resemble *(colonize, minimize, summarize, oxidize),* and in many instances this suffix has been properly attached to an adjective *(stabilize, neutralize, visualize). Homogenize* and *lyophilize* as technical terms for specific laboratory processes are so convenient they are widely used. But avoid thoughtless extension of this practice as in *inoculize, finalize, blendorize,* and *solubilize* (with variants *resolubilized, insolubilized,* and *solubilization*). These have nothing to recommend them in scientific writing. Such inventions as *rigidize, nebulize, automatize,* and *fiberize* (the last intended as a term to describe the effect of disintegrating a plant tissue in a Waring Blendor) are incomprehensible to anyone but their authors, and even they might have trouble defining them clearly. Business has blessed science with *percentagewise,* but science is responsible for *featurewise* and for experimenting with *re* as a prefix for new compound verbs; e.g., *rehydrolyze, rechromatograph, redissolve, reincubate.* Some of these are acceptable, others are clumsy or unnecessary.

Many writers use intransitive verbs, which do not take an object and have no passive voice, as if they were transitive, thus producing jargon: One cannot "react alcohol with acetic acid," or state that "alcohol was reacted with acetic acid," or have an "unreacted substance." Neither may one say that "the ether extract was migrated two-dimensionally."

Read your paper aloud to uncover tongue-twisters like "preformed performic acid was prepared," and such jingles as "cessation of saturation," "periodical general physical," and "conducted protracted." Do not use a word unlisted in the dictionary, unless it is understood in your field. Consider your foreign colleagues who must translate and try to understand what you have written.

Good Examples of Bad Habits

Here are some imperfections and possible corrections:

Abuse	*Correction*
Our research, designed to test the fatal effects of XXX on 10 dogs, was carried out by intravenously introducing the drug. In the experiments, a relatively small quantity, 3 cubic centimeters, was administered to each of 10 animals. In each case, XXX proved fatal, all dogs expiring before a lapse of five minutes after the injection.	Intravenous injection of 3 ml of XXX to each of 10 dogs killed the animals within 5 min.
A method, which was found to be expedient and not very difficult to accomplish and which possessed a high degree of accuracy in its results, was devised whereby . . .	An easy, accurate way to . . .
The quantitative findings reported by Smith were analyzed and seemed, according to our interpretation, to contain significant inconsistencies. Our reasons for attaining this diverse opinion are . . .	I think Smith's measurements are questionable because . . .
Of the utmost importance is the need to examine quantitatively the various instars which have not reached maturity, in order to evaluate and determine the validity of the theory advocated by Przibram.	To test Przibram's hypothesis, measure all instars.

Wordy	*Concise* (Kesling, 1958)
an innumerable number of tiny veins	innumerable tiny veins
Growth accelerates, as can be seen from the following Table (*or* Fig.)	Table (*or* Fig.) X shows, *or* Growth accelerates (Table X *or* Fig. X)
at the present moment (time)	now

Wordy	*Concise*
bright green in color	bright green
by means of	by, with
conducted inoculation experiments on	inoculated
contemporaneous in age	contemporaneous
created the possibility	made possible
due to the fact that	because
during the time that	while
equally as well	equally well
fewer in number	fewer
for the reason that	because, since
from the standpoint of	according to
goes under the name of	is called
if conditions are such that	if
in all cases	always
in order to	to
in terms of	in
in the event that	if
in view of the fact that	since, because
it is often the case that	often
it is possible that the cause is	the cause may be
it is this that	this
it would thus appear that	apparently
lenticular in character	lenticular
masses are of large size	masses are large
of such hardness that	so hard that
on the basis of	from, by, because
oval in shape *or* oval-shaped	oval
plants exhibited good growth	plants grew well
sacrifice (for kill)	kill
serves the function of being	is
subsequent to	after
the fish in question	this fish
the tests have not as yet	the tests have not
the treatment having been performed	after treatment
there can be little doubt that this is	this probably is

Wordy	*Concise*
they are both alike	they are alike
throughout the entire area	throughout the area
throughout the whole of the experiment	throughout the experiment
two equal halves	halves
we will always have a miscellany of quality in terms of illustrations	the quality of illustrations will always vary
with reference to	about
As already stated	
Concerning this matter it may be borne in mind that	
In this connection the statement may be made that	
It is interesting to note that	Omit such introductory phrases
It has long been known that	
It may be said that	
Typical results are shown	
With respect to the occurrence of these types, it has been found that	

Bad Reference	*Good Reference*
As far as my own observations are concerned, they show	My observations show
As far as this fauna is concerned, it	This fauna is
As for the frog, they are	Frogs are
It has not been possible to identify it with any of the described forms, and it seems to be so distinct that it is probable that additional examples could be recognized without difficulty	I could not identify it, but it is so distinct that one may easily recognize additional specimens.

Nonsense	*Sense*
This book fills a much-needed gap	This book is much needed
What we need is a list of biologists broken down by specialization	What we need is a list of biologists classified by specialties
While flying over Fort Churchill in	From a Polar Cub, flying over Fort

	Nonsense	*Sense*

Nonsense

a Polar Cub, two foxes were seen in a highly abnormal condition

On November 2, 1957, a porcupine was brought to the laboratory by a wildlife biologist in a moribund condition

Sense

Churchill, I saw two foxes in a highly abnormal condition

On 2 November 1957, a wildlife biologist brought a moribund porcupine to the laboratory

---

Spelling and Usage of Common Words

Consult *Webster's Third New International Dictionary* for spelling and division of words. Use the first choice where a choice is given. Use great care in spelling foreign names and words, making sure that accents and other diacritical marks (*see* p. 44) are correct. The following forms, including those that do not agree with *Webster's,* are considered good usage in biology.

acclimatize

acetylcholine, *no hyphen*

acknowledgment

after (later in time; subsequent), *see* following

agenda (things to be done or dealt with); *singular,* agendum

agglutinin-adsorption, *not* agglutinin-absorption

albumin (albumen means white of egg)

alga; *plural* algae

algal (adj)

aliquot, *better to substitute* "sample," "portion," *or* "fraction." (aliquot means integral fraction; strictly speaking, one cannot take a 3-ml aliquot from 10 ml of solution)

all right, *never* alright

amino acid, *no hyphen*

amoeba *or* ameba, for common term, but *Amoeba* as a generic name

ampoule, ampule, *preferred to* ampul

anaerobic, *not* anerobic

analogue

analyze

and/or, *avoid use of*

anesthesia, *not* anaesthesia

anticholinesterase, *one word*

autolyzate *or* autolysate

autolyze, *but* autolysis

autopsy (postmortem examination), *see* necropsy

bacillus; *plural,* bacilli (noun)

bacterial (adj)

bacterium; *plural,* bacteria (noun)

baker's yeast

base line, *not* baseline

basis; *plural,* bases

bioassay

biological, *preferred to* biologic

biopsy

biuret

blender; *but* Waring Blendor
brain stem *or* brainstem
breakdown (noun), break-up (noun)
brewer's yeast
bromothymol blue, *not*
    bromthymol blue
Büchner funnel, *not* Buchner
    [*from* Ernst Büchner]
Buchner hydraulic press juice
    [*from* Eduard Buchner]
burette *or* buret

cactus; *plural,* cacti
canceled, canceling
cancellation
cannot
carcass, carcasses
catalog *or* catalogue
catalyze
catecholamines
cellophan, cellophane
cholinesterase
cocarboxylase
coccus; *plural,* cocci
cod-liver oil
compared with *instead of* compared
    to (unless things compared are
    greatly dissimilar)
controlled, controlling
cooperate, cooperation
coordinate
corn oil
countercurrent
cover slip, *not* coverslip
co-worker
criterion; *plural,* criteria
criticize
cross-react (verb)

cross reaction (noun)
crystalline, crystallize
curriculum; *plural,* curricula
cytochrome *c, a,* etc.

dark-eyed, dark-haired (before a
    noun)
dark-field (adj)
darkroom (photography)
data *(plural); singular,* datum
daylight (time)
deep-rooted, deep-seated (before a
    noun)
deoxy (prefix), *not* desoxy
desiccate
desiccator
dialysis
dialyzation, dialyze
dipolar ion, *not* zwitter ion
disc, *preferred to* disk
distill
double-cross (noun *and* verb)
due to (as adjective should refer to
    noun; can be used with form of
    verb *to be*)

electron micrograph (or with
    hyphen)
embryo; *plural,* embryos
endemic (affecting few people, local)
end plate, end point
envelop (verb)
envelope (noun)
enzootic (affecting few animals,
    local)
enzymatic
epidemic (affecting many people at
    once, widespread)

epiphytotic (affecting many plants at once, widespread)

epizootic (affecting many animals at once, widespread)

equilibrium; *plural,* equilibria

estrous (adj), *not* oestrous

estrus (noun), *not* oestrus

extracellular, *no* hyphen

eyeball, eye color

eyepiece micrometer

farther (comparative of far)

feedback

fetus; *plural,* fetuses

flowmeter

fluorescent

focused, focusing

fold (words with the suffix *fold* are solid, except when Arabic numeral is used, as 14-fold)

following (immediately to be treated); *do not use for* after

foothill, footprint

forefoot, forelimb

former and latter (*avoid,* and *never use* when referring to more than two antecedents in a sentence)

formula; *plural,* formulas

fourfold; *see* fold

fractions, *use* hyphen in one-half, one-third, etc., as adjectives, *but use* decimal system with Arabic numerals, as 0.5, 0.33, etc., when followed by a unit of measurement; e.g., 0.5 ml

free (suffix), *hyphenate*

free from, *not* free of

freeze-dried

freezing point

fuller's earth

fungal *or* fungous (adj)

fungus (noun); *plural,* fungi

further (in addition)

gall bladder

gallnut

gastrointestinal

gauge

gelatin, *not* gelatine

genus; *plural,* genera

germ cell

gladiolus; *plural,* gladioli *or* gladioluses (but *Gladiolus* **as** generic name)

glycerin, *use* glycerol

gram-negative (adj)

Gram stain

gray (grey in British usage)

half-life (noun and adj)

halftone (in engraving)

hemorrhage, *preferred to* haemorrhage

hind foot, hind limb

homologue, *not* homolog

hydrolysis (noun); *plural,* hydrolyses

hydrolyze (verb), hydrolyzate *or* hydrolysate (noun)

hypothesis; *plural,* hypotheses

hypothesize, *not* hypothecate

index; *plural,* indexes *or* indices (of refraction, mathematical)

indole

infrared

innocuous (adj)
inoculate
inoculum; *plural,* inocula
insanitary (adj)
intra-arterial
intracardiac
intracellular

juvenile (noun, adj)

Kjeldahl, kjeldahlize
kneecap, knee-deep
Krebs cycle
Krebs-Ringer solution

label, labeled
landfall, landlocked
leukemia, *preferred to* leucemia
leukocyte, *preferred to* leucocyte
lifelike, life-size, lifetime
like (words with the suffix *like* are
    solid, except where "l" is doubled
    or tripled, as in shell-like, or in
    long words, as
    pleuropneumonia-like)
lipid (noun), *not* lipide, lipin,
    lipoid
lipoic acid, *not* thioctic acid
lipoid (adj)
lipoprotein
liquefy

mannite, *use* mannitol
matrix; *plural,* matrices
maximal (adj); *or* maximum
maximum (noun); *plural,* maxima
medium; *plural,* media
micro-Kjeldahl

micromethod
microorganism
midsummer
millennium
minimal (adj); *or* minimum
minimum (noun); *plural,* minima
mold (noun, verb); *not* mould
mucin
mucous (adj), mucus (noun)
multicolored

necropsy (postmortem examination)
Nessler reagent *and* Nessler test, *but*
    nesslerize
ninhydrin
non (most words with this prefix
    are solid; exceptions are proper
    nouns)

oasis; *plural,* oases
off-color, *but* offshoot, offshore
optimal (adj)
optimum (noun) ; *plural,* optima
overall (noun), over-all (adj)
owing to; *see* due to
oxaloacetic acid

pandemic (widely epidemic in
    people)
panzootic (widely zootic in animals)
papergram, *use* paper chromatogram
per cent, *use symbol* (%) *with
    number*
percentage (e.g., the percentage of
    cells)
per mil, *use symbol* ($^0/_{00}$) *with
    number*
per millage (noun)

petri dish
phagocytosis (noun), *but* phagocytize (verb)
phenomenon; *plural,* phenomena
photochemistry
photomicrograph (in microscopy) *not* microphotograph
phylum; *plural,* phyla
pipette *or* pipet
poly, post, pre (most words with these combining forms are solid)
protozoa; *singular,* protozoon (*but* Protozoa as phylum)
protozoan (adj)

radioactive
radioautograph, *not* autoradiograph
radioisotope
radius; *plural,* radii
Ringer solution

self (prefix), *hyphenate*
separating funnel, separatory funnel
septum; *plural,* septa
serum; *plural,* sera
skillful
sporeforming
steam-distill
stopcock
sub (prefix), *no hyphen*
syllabus; *plural,* syllabi

tapeworm
taproot, tap water
taxon; *plural,* taxa

technique, technic
thiamine
thioctic acid, *use* lipoic acid
thioglycolate
threefold; *see* fold
thyroxine
titer
toothrow
trichloroacetic, *not* trichloracetic
tryptophan (*no final* e)
turnover-number
Tween 80 = polyoxyethylene sorbitan monooleate (use capital and chemical name first time in text)
twofold; *see* fold

U-shaped (adj); U shape (noun)
ultra (most words with this prefix are solid, as ultracentrifuge, ultraviolet)
urethan

vertebra; *plural,* vertebrae

wavelength
weekday
while (of time) , *avoid using as conjunction instead of* although, and, but, whereas
wildlife

X-ray (adj and noun)

Y-shaped, Y form

Punctuation

A good style (proper words in proper places) may require less punctuation than a bad one; punctuation must not be expected to do the work that proper word order might do better. No matter how you word and punctuate a sentence, you supposedly know what it means; but you must consider whether your meaning will be equally clear to others. If a sentence requires excessive punctuation, rewrite it or divide it into two or more sentences.

PERIOD

1) Use a period (full stop)
    a) after a declarative or explanatory sentence
    b) as a decimal point
    c) after certain abbreviations: W. B. Jones, Fig., p. (page, pages), and most abbreviations of Latin words (e.g., i.e., et al.)
2) Use three spaced periods (ellipsis) to indicate an omission of a word or group of words within a sentence of quoted material. Leave a space before and after the ellipsis: "Mary had a . . . lamb." If the omitted words begin a sentence, do not use an ellipsis. If the omitted words conclude a sentence, place the ellipsis before the period . . . . If the omitted words are the first part of a second sentence in the quotation, place the ellipsis after the period. . . . Notice the spacing after the word *period* in the two preceding examples. If a paragraph is omitted in the quotation, use a whole line of periods. (Some publications use three asterisks.)
3) Omit the period after
    a) capital-letter abbreviations of names of countries (USSR, USA), government agencies (AEC, NSF, USDA, NIH), societies (AAAS, AIBS, CBE), international agencies (WHO, UNESCO), compass directions (NW), and biochemical compounds (DNA)
    b) contractions used as abbreviations (exptl, 22nd) and symbols for chemical elements (C, H, O, Cl) and units of measurement (mg, ml, μg)
    c) titles, headings, and major subheadings, except run-in subheadings; legends for tables
    d) items in lists
4) In special situations, place the period
    a) inside the quotation marks when a sentence ends with a quoted phrase, even when the period is not part of the quotation
    b) inside or outside parentheses or brackets, depending on whether the parenthetical matter is an independent sentence (the period

goes inside) or is a subordinate part of the main sentence (the period goes outside)

CENTERED OR RAISED PERIOD

Use a centered period for

1) water of hydration in chemical formulas ($Na_2B_4O_7 \cdot 10H_2O$)
2) multiplication when equations are too crowded to permit use of the times sign ($\times$) or when use of closed-up or thinly spaced symbols is not satisfactory; for example, $k \times g \times (a + 2)$ may be printed $kg(a+2)$ or $k \cdot g \cdot (a+2)$ or $k \cdot g(a+2)$
3) chemical bonds if the standard bond sign occupies too much space: $R \cdot CH_3$ *for* $R—CH_3$
4) genetic expressions: $AA \cdot AB \cdot BB$, etc.

COMMA

The comma provides separation or brief pause within a sentence and is helpful in grouping words, phrases, and clauses for clarity and ease of reading. Do not separate a subject and its verb or a verb and its object, except by phrases between commas. Noun phrases can act as subjects and objects and should not be set off with commas.

1) Use a comma
   a) to separate two independent clauses joined by a coordinating conjunction (*and, but, either, neither, or, nor*). (But *see* 2a below; *see also* p. 24.) If the clauses contain internal punctuation, separate them with a semicolon
   b) to set off a dependent introductory clause begun with a subordinating conjunction (*if, although, since, when, where, while, because*)
   c) to separate words or phrases in apposition if necessary for clarity
   d) to separate the elements (clauses, words, or phrases) in a series. If an element already contains other internal punctuation, separate it from other elements with a semicolon. (If a series is constructed grammatically, the parts will be parallel—that is, each part can be read separately in the sentence without loss of sense.)
   e) to separate nonrestrictive (nondefining) clauses or phrases from the rest of the sentence. (Nonrestrictive clauses or phrases give extra information that is not essential to the meaning of the sentence. If you are uncertain whether the phrase or clause is restrictive, read the sentence without it; if the meaning is materially altered, the element is restrictive.)

  f) to separate conjunctive adverbs (*therefore, thus, then, still, however, accordingly, moreover, nevertheless, consequently*) and transitional phrases (*on the contrary* [*but* may do the work as well], *on the other hand, in fact, after all, in the first place* [*first* is better])

  g) to set off a short quotation. If the quotation is long, use a colon

  h) to set off contrasted words, phrases, or other elements. "It is . . . , not . . . ,"; "The greater . . . , the less . . . ."

  i) to separate words, phrases, and clauses used parenthetically or placed out of their natural position for emphasis or clarity. ("Keys provide, except in the most specialized works, a useful means . . . .")

  j) to separate adjacent sets of figures. "In 1935, 100 experiments . . . ."

  k) to group numbers in thousands: 1,000; 18,000; 1,000,000

2) Omit the comma

  a) if two independent clauses joined by a coordinating conjunction are short, and if no ambiguity results

  b) after a short introductory phrase begun with a preposition, if no ambiguity results

  c) around short appositives. "The species *Bombyx mori* . . . ." "The respiratory quotient RQ is . . . ."

  d) after equations and formulas set off from the text by centering on the page

3) Place the comma

  a) inside the closing quotation marks when a sentence continues beyond the end of the quoted phrase, even when the comma is not a part of the quotation

  b) after a period that follows an abbreviation if the sentence requires a comma. Do not expect the period to do its own work and substitute for the comma also.

SEMICOLON The semicolon is a mark of coordination and therefore should not be used with dependent clauses.

1) Use the semicolon to separate

  a) coordinate clauses not joined by a conjunction

  b) coordinate elements or elements of a series if they contain internal punctuation

  c) coordinate clauses joined by a conjunctive adverb (*however, moreover, also, then*) (Clauses introduced by subordinating conjunctions [*because, whereas, inasmuch*] are separated by commas.)

2) Place the semicolon outside the quotation mark

COLON   1) Use a colon
    a) to introduce a long quotation (a comma is sufficient for a short one)
    b) to introduce a list or enumeration not immediately preceded by a verb or preposition
    c) to emphasize a sequence in thought between two complete sentences when the emphasis obtained by a period or word, such as *namely,* is insufficient
    d) to separate a complete clause from a following illustrative clause or phrase
    e) to separate parts of ratios (The slant line also serves this function if there are only two elements in the ratio, but do not use the slant line in a ratio containing three or more elements.)
    f) in literature citations to separate volume and page numbers
  2) Place the colon outside the quotation mark

QUESTION MARK   1) Use a question mark at the end of a direct question, even if the question is presented in declarative form
  2) Do not use a question mark after an indirect question
  3) Place the question mark inside the quotation mark if the question mark is part of the quotation, or outside if the mark is not part of the quotation

EXCLAMATION POINT   The exclamation point is rarely justified in scientific writing. Exceptions: in place of *sic* or a mark of affirmation in older taxonomic work, and as a factorial symbol in mathematics: $(x-2)/6!$

DASHES   1) Use the em dash sparingly (in typing copy indicate an em dash by two unspaced hyphens)
    a) to indicate an abrupt break or shift in thought
    b) to isolate parenthetical matter (as parentheses are used, *but see* Parentheses)
    c) within brackets within parentheses for a third level of interpolation (The house sparrow [common in bushes—shun this cumbersome construction—as well as trees] is a bird.)
  2) Use an en dash (half the length of an em dash, a single hyphen on typewriter) between numbers to indicate range (e.g., pages in a citation,

33:9–14; *but* from page 6 to 8, *not* from page 6–8). Do not use a minus sign and an en dash together: −4 to −5 C, *not* −4−−5 C

PARENTHESES

1) Use parentheses
   a) to set off comment or explanation that is structurally independent of the sentence. (Parentheses indicate a greater independence than dashes or commas.)
   b) to group mathematical expressions
   c) to label enumerations included within a paragraph. "The four steps were (i) . . . , (ii) . . . , (iii) . . . , and (iv) . . . ." (but do not label the enumerations unless necessary). (*See* Enumeration and Series, p. 24)
2) Avoid use of double parentheses: (. . . (. . .) . . .). *See* Brackets, below and Dashes, p. 21
3) Use single parentheses to set off enumerated paragraphs: 1), a), i)

BRACKETS

Use brackets
1) to set off words or other matter you have inserted in a quotation
2) around parenthetical remarks inserted within other parenthetical remarks
3) to set off bibliographic details not shown in the original

APOSTROPHE

1) Use an apostrophe
   a) and *s* (*'s*) to form the possessive of a singular noun, but the apostrophe alone to form the possessive of a plural noun ending in *s*
   b) to indicate omission of letters in a contraction; but contractions such as can't, don't, and won't are inappropriate in scientific writing. No apostrophe is used in an abbreviation or symbol
   c) and *s* to form the plural of letters, figures, and some words. "He uses too many *but*'s"
2) Do not use an apostrophe in certain well-established geographic names (Pikes Peak) or in names of some organizations (Teachers Association), where the qualifying word has the force of an adjective rather than a possessive noun

QUOTATION MARKS

1) Use double quotation marks in the text around
   a) all direct quotations
   b) titles of articles, parts of books, and series titles
   c) new technical terms or old terms used in a new or unusual sense

   2) Use single quotation marks around a word, title, or term within a quotation

   3) Special situations

     a) If a quotation extends over more than one paragraph, begin each paragraph with a quotation mark, but close the quotation only at the end of the last paragraph

     b) Relationship to other punctuation. (i) Place a comma or period inside the closing quotation mark, even if it is not part of the quotation. (ii) Place the colon and semicolon outside the quotation marks. (iii) Place the question mark and dashes inside the closing quotation mark when they belong to the quotation, outside if they do not

HYPHEN   1) Use a hyphen

     a) between the numerator and denominator of a fraction when spelled out (one-third)

     b) between the parts of some compound words (*see* p. 25; *see also Webster's* dictionary, under *The Writing of Compounds,* p. 30a, for discussion of hyphen)

     c) between numbers to indicate a range; the printer will use an en dash. But in running text *to* is preferable (*see* Dashes, p. 21)

  2) Avoid use of hyphen

     a) between parts of a compound modifier if the modifier follows the noun modified (the scientist was well known)

     b) between words of a well-established open compound noun that is used to modify a substantive (sodium chloride solution, *or* house sparrow population)

SLANT LINE (SOLIDUS, VIRGULE, SLASH, OR SHILLING BAR)

Since the slant line (/) is a mathematical mark of division ($3/4 = \frac{3}{4}$), it must be used with care.

  1) It may be used instead of a colon to indicate ratio (3/4 or 3:4), but not in a ratio involving more than two elements. (The ratio 1:3:4 is clear; 1/3/4 is mathematically ambiguous)

  2) Do not use the slant line as shorthand for *per* if more than one is required (1.5 pc/km²/yr), because it is mathematically ambiguous. To abbreviate "The strontium fallout was 1.5 picocuries per square kilometer per year," use the form "The strontium fallout was 1.5 pc/square kilometer per year," *or* "1.5 pc/ (square kilometer × year)"

Careful writers are increasingly using negative exponents to show units in the denominator: 1.5pc km^{-2} year $^{-1}$, 5 cm^2 sec^{-1}, 10 g cm^{-2}

3) Avoid such expressions as *and/or* and *signal/noise ratio*. The expression "The cultures were subjected to light and/or dark" can be expressed by "The cultures were subjected to light, or dark, or both." Use a hyphenated compound, *signal-to-noise ratio,* instead of *signal/noise ratio.*

PUNCTUATION OF LITERATURE CITED

Follow the style indicated on pages 74 to 82. Separate the main parts of the citation—author, date, article title, journal (or book name, publisher and address), and volume and page numbers—with periods. Use a comma after author's surname followed by initials and between publisher's name and city. Use a colon after the volume number or issue number. Omit issue number unless the issues are paged separately; use parentheses around issue numbers accompanying a volume number. Use a hyphen between extreme page numbers of a citation, and between dates when necessary. (The printer will set this as an en dash.)

ENUMERATION AND SERIES

Series may range from three one-word elements to complex enumerations, each element of which may require a separate sentence or paragraph. If a complex series seems necessary, the elements may be kept in proper order by use of indicative words such as *then, when, afterward,* and *finally.* In a series, simple or complex, the elements should be constructed in parallel. For example, the sentence "The mixture was heated, shaken, centrifuged, and the supernatant fluid frozen" is not properly constructed, for the last element cannot be read as part of the series. The first three elements make up a series, but the last must become a coordinate clause with a verb: "The mixture was heated, shaken, and centrifuged; the supernatant fluid was frozen."

1) Punctuate all simple series with commas
   a) "The mixture was heated, shaken, and centrifuged"
   b) "The mixture was heated to 40 C, shaken at 30 cycles per sec, and centrifuged at 18,000 × *g*"
2) Punctuate more complex series (those in which the individual elements contain their own punctuation) with semicolons
   a) "The mixture was heated at 40 C for 10 min to inactivate..., which...; shaken at 30 cycles per sec; and centrifuged at 18,000 × *g*"

b) "The mixture was heated, shaken, and centrifuged; the pellet was discarded; and the supernatant fluid was quick-frozen and stored for 3 days at −10 C"

3) If a still more complex series and subseries combination is required, enumerate each element in the main series with a small Roman numeral in parentheses, (i), (ii), (iii), separate the parts of the main series with semicolons, and punctuate the subseries with commas. If necessary, go a step further and make each part of the enumerated main series into one or more sentences

4) In extremely complex series, paragraph enumeration may be required. Begin each paragraph with an Arabic numeral and a single, closing parenthesis

---

Compound Words and Derivatives

A compound consists of two or more words joined together, with or without a hyphen. A compound word expresses an idea different in meaning or function from the ideas expressed by the individual parts (*black bird,* possibly a crow; *blackbird*).

Two questions must be answered in determining whether a compound should be formed: (i) is compounding desirable? and (ii) should a hyphen be used? Compound words are used commonly in scientific writing without hyphens, but occasionally a hyphen is needed to avoid a confusing sequence of letters or a jumble of ideas (*cell-like*; *freeze-dry*; *red-ear sunfish*).

A few examples of styling for compounds and derivatives are cited below: further information may be found in *Webster's* dictionary under *The Writing of Compounds,* p. 30a.

1) Noun compounds are usually separate when the two elements are both accented (e.g., *buffalo fish, oak wood, subject matter*), solid when the term has a special meaning and when one of the elements has lost its accent (as *northwest, pineapple, paperback, blackboard*), and hyphenated when the elements are short and lower case (*ox-bow*) or the names of a technical unit of measurement (*gram-centimeter, light-year*) .

2) Verb compounds in which the second element (noun or pronoun) is the direct object of the verb are usually solid (*killjoy*), unless confusing letters result and a hyphen is indicated (*cure-all*). A verb compound consisting of two verbs is hyphenated (*has-been*).

3) An adjective compound is frequently hyphenated when placed before the word it modifies, but when the same combination is written after

the word a hyphen is omitted: ... a *well-known* method; ... a method *well known* in biology

But this rule does not apply when simple technical terms or well-established open compound nouns are used as adjectives:

... a *sodium chloride* solution; ... a solution of *sodium chloride*; a *house sparrow* population, a population of *house sparrows*

When a numeral forms an element of a compound adjective a hyphen is recommended:

... two *2-liter* flasks   ... a can of *10-ml* pipettes
    ... *two-thirds* majority

Compound adjectives with such endings as *born, bred, fold, like,* and *proof,* are usually solid.

4) An adverb ending in *ly* is not hyphenated when it is the first element of a two-word modifier:

... a *quickly* completed reaction ... *naturally* occurring substance
   ... a *carefully* preserved specimen

5) Words in which prefixes, suffixes, or combining forms appear are derivatives rather than compounds. Derivatives are usually set solid. A few exceptions are (i) prefixes that may cause confusion because they end with a vowel and the base word begins with the same letter (*anti-intellectualism, semi-independent*); (ii) prefixes before words that begin with a capital (*pre-English; un-American;* but, in geology, *Precambrian*); (iii) prefixes that govern two or more words (*ex-*vice president, *self-*appointed leader); (iv) prefixes that, if set solid with the base element, would form a word easily confused with another (*recreation, re-creation; un-ionized, unionized*); and (v) suffixes that when added to the base word would form a succession of three identical consonants (*bell-like, hull-less*) or a word of several syllables (*pleuropneumonia-like*).

6) Certain scientific societies approve lists of common or vernacular names of animals and plants that are compound words. Adopt these names because they represent good usage (*see* p. 69).

Numerals The following are acceptable rules for the use of numerals in running text:

1) Use numerals whenever a number is followed by a standard unit of measurement, such as *gram, meter, milliliter, hour,* or *curie,* or its abbreviation.

2) Otherwise use words through *nine* and numerals for larger numbers

(nine animals; *14* parts); but in a series containing some numbers under 10 and others over, use numerals for all. Treat ordinal numbers in the same manner (third, 33rd).

3) In very large numbers, substitute a word for part of the number (1.6 million, not 1,600,000), or add appropriate prefixes such as *mega, kilo, micro,* and *milli* to the basic unit of measurement. Powers of 10 may also be used. (*See below.*)

4) Always use numerals for dates, page numbers, and numerical designations, percentages, and expressions of time, as: 1 January 1963 (*or* 1 Jan. 1963); page 822; type 1; 10:15 PM; 27%.

5) Avoid beginning a sentence with a numeral.

Metric and Decimal Systems

The metric system for measures and weights is recommended in scientific writing because of its world-wide acceptance. In accordance with action taken by the 12th General Assembly of the International Union of Biological Sciences at Rome, 12 to 14 April 1955, the decimal system rather than fractions should be used in scientific publications.

The units of the metric system are the *meter* for linear measure, the *are* (100 m²) for surface area, the *liter* (0.001 m³ of space) for capacity, and the *gram* (1 ml of water at 4 C) for weight. In the metric system, weights and measures larger and smaller than the *meter,* the *are,* the *liter,* and the *gram* are related to these units by the decimal system as follows (International Committee on Weights and Measures, 1962):

Multiples and Submultiples	Prefixes	Pronunciation	Symbols
$1,000,000,000,000 = 10^{12}$	tera	ter'a	T
$1,000,000,000 = 10^{9}$	giga	ji'ga	G
$1,000,000 = 10^{6}$	mega	meg'a	M
$1,000 = 10^{3}$	kilo	kil'o	k
$100 = 10^{2}$	hecto	hek'to	h
$10 = 10$	deka	dek'a	dk
[The unit = one]			
$0.1 = 10^{-1}$	deci	des'i	d
$0.01 = 10^{-2}$	centi	sen'ti	c
$0.001 = 10^{-3}$	milli	mil'i	m
$0.000\ 001 = 10^{-6}$	micro	mi'kro	μ
$0.000\ 000\ 001 = 10^{-9}$	nano	nan'o	n
$0.000\ 000\ 000\ 001 = 10^{-12}$	pico	pe'co	p
$0.000\ 000\ 000\ 000\ 001 = 10^{-15}$	femto	fem'to	f
$0.000\ 000\ 000\ 000\ 000\ 001 = 10^{-18}$	atto	at'to	a

Examples of the metric measures and weights and their equivalents are given in Tables 1 and 2.

TABLE 1. *Metric measures and weights with common equivalents*

Length

Myriameter	10^4 m		6.213	miles
Kilometer* (km)	10^3 m		0.621	mile
Hectometer	10^2 m		109.3	yards
Dekameter	10 m		10.93	yards
Meter* (m)	1 m		3.28	feet
Decimeter	10^{-1} m		3.937	inches
Centimeter* (cm)	10^{-2} m		0.394	inch
Millimeter* (mm)	10^{-3} m		39×10^{-3}	inch
Micron* (μ)	10^{-6} m *or* 10^{-3} mm		39×10^{-6}	inch
Millimicron* (mμ) *or*	10^{-3} μ		39×10^{-9}	inch
Nanometer	10^{-9} m		39×10^{-9}	inch
Micromicron ($\mu\mu$) *or*	10^{-6} μ		39×10^{-12}	inch
Picometer	10^{-12} m		39×10^{-12}	inch

Surface

Hectare* (ha)	10^4 m²		2.471 acres
Are	10^2 m²	119.6 square yards	0.025 acre

Capacity

Kiloliter	10^3 liters	1 m³	1.308 cubic yards	264.18 gallons
Hectoliter	10^2 liters	10^{-1} m³	2.838 bushels	26.42 gallons
Dekaliter	10 liters	10^{-2} m³	1.135 pecks	2.64 gallons
Liter* (liter)	1 liter	10^{-3} m³	61.02 cubic inches	1.05 quarts
Deciliter	10^{-1} liter	10^{-4} m³	6.1 cubic inches	0.10 quart
Centiliter	10^{-2} liter	10^{-5} m³	0.61 cubic inch	0.33 ounce
Milliliter* (ml)	10^{-3} liter	10^{-6} m³ *or* 1 cm³	61×10^{-3} cubic inch	0.27 dram
Microliter* (μl)	10^{-6} liter	10^{-9} m³ *or* 1 mm³	61×10^{-6} cubic inch	0.27×10^{-3} dram

Weight

Metric ton* (ton)	10^3 kg	1 m³ water, 4 C	1.1 tons
Myriagram	10^4 g	1 dekaliter water, 4 C	22.04 pounds
Kilogram* (kg)	10^3 g	1 liter water, 4 C	2.20 pounds
Hectogram	10^2 g	1 deciliter water, 4 C	3.52 ounces

* Most commonly used units.

Weight (Table 1 Continued)

Dekagram	10 g	10 cm³ water, 4 C	0.35 ounce
Gram* (g)	1 g	1 cm³ water, 4 C	15.43 grains
Decigram	10^{-1} g	0.1 cm³ water, 4 C	1.54 grains
Centigram	10^{-2} g	10 mm³ water, 4 C	0.15 grain
Milligram* (mg)	10^{-3} g	1 mm³ water, 4 C	15×10^{-3} grain
Microgram* (μg)	10^{-6} g *or* 10^{-3} mg	10^{-3} mm³ water, 4 C	15×10^{-6} grain
Millimicrogram (mμg) *or*	10^{-3} μg	10^{-6} mm³ water, 4 C	15×10^{-9} grain
Nanogram	10^{-9} g		

* Most commonly used units.

TABLE 2. *Common measures and weights with metric equivalents*

Inch	2.54	cm	Cord	3.625	m³
Foot	30.48	cm	(128 cubic feet)		
Yard	0.914	m	Pint, liquid, US	0.473	liter
Fathom (2 yards)	1.829	m	(16 oz)		
Rod (5½ yards)	5.029	m	Quart, liquid, US (32 oz)	0.946	liter
Furlong (220 yards)	201.16	m	Quart, dry, US (2 pints)	1.101	liters
Mile, statute	1.609	km	Quart, imperial (40 oz)	1.136	liters
(1,760 yards)			Gallon, US (4 quarts)	3.785	liters
Mile, nautical	1.854	km	Gallon, imperial	4.546	liters
(2,026 yards)			Peck, dry, US (8 quarts)	8.809	liters
Square inch	6.452	cm²	Peck, dry, imperial	9.092	liters
Square foot	0.092	m²	Bushel, dry, US (4 pecks)	35.24	liters
Square yard	0.836	m²	Bushel, imperial	36.37	liters
Square rod	25.29	m²	Pound, avdp (16 oz)	453.592	g
Square mile	2.59	km²	Pound, troy (12 oz)	373.24	g
(640 acres)			Ounce, avdp (16 drams)	28.35	g
Acre	40.468	ares	Ounce, troy (480 grains)	31.103	g
Cubic inch	16.387	cm³	Dram, avdp	1.177	g
Cubic foot	0.028	m³	Grain, troy	0.065	g
(1,728 cubic inches)			Carat (precious stones)	0.200	g
Cubic yard	0.7646	m³	Ton, long	1.016	metric ton
(27 cubic feet)			(2,240 pounds)		
Board foot	0.0025	m³	Ton, short	0.907	metric ton
(144 cubic inches)			(2,000 pounds)		

Use the Celsius scale whenever practical, rather than the Fahrenheit, to indicate temperature.

Geographic and Geologic Names

For geographic names refer to the *U.S. Government Printing Office Style Manual, Lippincott Gazetteer of the World, Rand McNally World Atlas,* the *Times* [London] *Atlas,* the latest maps published by federal or state agencies, or lists published by the Board on Geographic Names, Office of Geography, U.S. Department of the Interior.

Do not abbreviate names of divisions of the earth's surface (Arctic Circle, South Pole); continents (Africa, Asia, South America); countries (North Vietnam, South Korea), except USA and USSR; regions (Sahara, Middle West, Orient) ; islands; oceans, seas, lakes and rivers; or mountains (Pyrenees, Himalaya). Names of certain cities and geographic regions of biological significance have had English spellings for many years, and these have also become conventional names. Use these spellings. A few examples with the official or local name in parentheses are as follows:

Alexandria (El Iskandariya), Egypt
Athens (Athinai), Greece
Bangkok (Krung Thep), Thailand
Beirut (Beyrouth), Lebanon
Belgrade (Beograd), Yugoslavia
Breslau (Wroclaw), Poland
Bucharest (Bucuresti), Romania
Cairo (El Qahira), Egypt
Canton (Kwangchow), China
Cologne (Köln), Germany
Copenhagen (København), Denmark
Damascus (Damas), Syria
Florence (Firenze), Italy
Hankow (Wuhan), China
Havana (Habana), Cuba
Ireland (Eire)
Kiev (Kiyev), USSR
Lisbon (Lisboa), Portugal
Moscow (Moskva), USSR
Munich (München), Germany
Naples (Napoli), Italy
Peking (Peiching; also formerly Peiping), China
Prague (Praha), Czechoslovakia
Rome (Roma), Italy
Seoul (Kyongsong), Korea
Sofia (Sofiya), Bulgaria
Taipei (Taihoku), Formosa
Venice (Venezia), Italy
Vienna (Wien), Austria
Warsaw (Warszawa), Poland

United States and foreign geological names and terms should be used in accordance with the stratigraphic records of the Geologic Names Committee, U.S. Geological Survey. Table 3 shows the accepted names (1957) for eras, systems or periods, and series or epochs. The standard letter symbols used on geologic maps are given in parentheses.

TABLE 3.   *Major stratigraphic and geological time divisions in use by the U.S. Geological Survey*

Era	System or Period Name	System or Period Symbol	Series or Epoch	Approximate Time Boundaries in Millions of Years
Cenozoic	Quaternary	(Q)	Recent	
			Pleistocene	1
	Tertiary	(T)	Pliocene	10-13
			Miocene	25
			Oligocene	36-40
			Eocene	58-60
			Paleocene	63
Mesozoic	Cretaceous	(K)	Upper, Lower	125
	Jurassic	(J)	Upper, Middle, Lower	150
	Triassic	(T_R)	Upper, Middle, Lower	180
Paleozoic	Permian	(P)		205
	Pennsylvanian	(℟*)	Upper, Middle, Lower	
	Mississippian	(M*)	Upper, Lower	255
	Devonian	(D)	Upper, Middle, Lower	315
	Silurian	(S)	Upper, Middle, Lower	350-425
	Ordovician	(O)	Upper, Middle, Lower	430-500
	Cambrian	(Є)	Upper, Middle, Lower	510
Precambrian		(pЄ)	Upper, Middle, Lower	3,000

* The letter C is used to designate Carboniferous systems in regions where Pennsylvanian and Mississippian systems are not differentiated.

Minor stratigraphic units, and words known locally, are not abbreviated or capitalized. Examples: formation, dome, coal beds, slate, fault, East

Texas oil field, currelly vein. Names of the great soil groups are capitalized: Alpine Meadow, Bog, Chernozem, Desert, Podzol (ashlike), Prairie, Tundra.

Abbreviations and Symbols

Abbreviations consist of one or more letters (rarely more than four) to which words and phrases have been reduced by contraction or omission. Use them sparingly and only if of advantage to the reader. Follow the standards listed on p. 34 to 41. Form new ones only when you can save a significant amount of space without placing an unnecessary burden on the reader's memory. Define all new or unusual abbreviations the first time you use them in a paper. Do not repeat them monotonously when pronouns or other substitutes may be employed. Ordinarily a sentence should not begin with an abbreviation.

Short words for units of measurement, such as *acre, cent, chain, day, inch, liter, mile, rod, ton, week,* and *year,* should ordinarily be spelled out. When in doubt, spell it out.

The same abbreviation is used for both singular and plural, as "1 mm" and "3 mm," but, when an abbreviation is used in a sentence, the verbs should agree with the quantity: thus, "1 mm is" and "3 mm are." Letters in abbreviations such as DNA are not spaced. Omit periods after letters except where confusion might result, or after abbreviations of certain Latin words. Thus "no. 10" for number ten, "Fig." for figure, "et al." for *et alii,* "N.Y." for New York, but "3:30 PM" for afternoon.

Do not abbreviate names of countries, except USA and USSR. In the text, abbreviate state names (except Alaska, Hawaii, Idaho, Iowa, Maine, Ohio, Texas, and Utah) and district names immediately after any geographic term: Rochester, N.Y.; Cambridge, Mass.; Mexico, D.F.; Washington, D.C. Do not abbreviate state names standing alone or English translations of geographic names of foreign origin (*see* p. 30). Abbreviations for geologic terms should conform to those proposed by the Geologic Names Committee, U.S. Geological Survey (*see* p. 31).

Since confusion has arisen over certain abbreviations, the following words and terms should be spelled out: cocarboxylase, dinitrophenol, enzymatic activity, hydrocortisone, naphthaleneacetic acid, nicotinamide, thiamine, tricarboxylic acid cycle (and the members thereof), trichloroacetic acid, pantothenic acid and its salts, pteroylglutamate, pyridoxal, pyridoxamine, deoxypyridoxamine. Spell out names of amino acids, peptides, carbohydrates, and all other words and phrases not widely used in several branches of science.

Do not use abbreviations in the title or abstract of a paper. Titles and abstracts are often translated into foreign languages, and undefined or uncommon abbreviations may lead to confusion.

Abbreviate terms denoting units of weight and measurement in the text only when preceded by numerals; thus, *gram, meter, milliliter, molar,* but "10 g," "100 m," "25 ml," and "0.1 м." Use the decimal system for units of concentration, etc.; thus, 0.1 м, not м/10. Conventional signs and symbols for certain abbreviations are permitted in the text; thus the slant line (/) for "per" (if only one is required, *see* p. 23) and % with an Arabic numeral for "per cent." Do not use the ambiguous term *milligrams per cent*; use instead mg/100 ml, mg/100 **ml,** mg/100 g, as appropriate.

Abbreviations may be used with tables, maps, specifications, and figures, but if they are unusual they should be defined in footnote, legend, or nearby text.

Spell out scientific names of organisms in the titles of papers and abstracts. In the text spell out generic names when first used in combination with a specific name. Thereafter they may be abbreviated to their first letter unless confusion results. Never abbreviate generic names when used alone: thus, *Ascaris* and *Zea,* not *A.* and *Z.* For abbreviations of new genus (*genus novum*), new species (*species nova*), and new variety (*varietas nova*) the Latin "gen. n.," "sp. n.," and "var. n." are preferable to the English forms "n. gen.," "n. sp.," and "n. var.," because the name of a new taxon is **Latin** (a Latin synopsis of any new plant taxon must be furnished). Latin is recommended for *nomen conservandum* (plural, *nomina conservanda*), *nomen nudum* (plural, *nomina nuda*), and *nomen rejiciendum* (plural, *nomina rejicienda*).

Do not abbreviate names of enzymes. Avoid such usage as ATPase, RNase, and DNase or DNAase for adenosine triphosphatase, ribonuclease, and deoxyribonuclease.

Many special abbreviations are in common use. For example, standard definitions and symbols used in respiratory physiology are available (Federation Proc. **9:** 602–605, 1950), and terms used in radiation biology are being considered for adoption by international groups. Other abbreviations may be found in dictionaries. Some journals give lists of acceptable abbreviations in their "Instructions to Authors."

The following abbreviations and symbols are acceptable in biology. Most are taken from the American Standards Association *Abbreviations for Scientific and Engineering Terms* (Bulletin Y1, Z10.1–1941). Abbreviate units of measure only when used with numerals.

A

about (*circa*)	ca.
absolute	abs
absorbancy*	*A*
acetic acid, 2,4-dichloro - phenoxy	2,4-D
acre	*spell out*
adenosine diphosphate [5(pyro-) diphosphate of adenosine]	ADP
adenosine monophosphate (needed for contrast with 2'-, and 3'-phospates = 2'-AMP, 3'-AMP)	AMP
adenosine triphosphatase (enzyme)	*spell out*
adenosine triphosphate [5(pyro-) triphosphate of adenosine]	ATP
adenylic acid, *see* adenosine monophosphate	
ad libitum (as desired)	ad lib.
adrenocorticotropin	ACTH
afternoon (*post meridiem*)	PM
against (*versus*)	vs.
alternating-current (adj)	a-c
altitude	alt

amount	amt
ampere(s)	amp
ampere-hour	amp-hr
and elsewhere (*et alibi*)	et al.
and others (*et alii*)	et al.
and the rest (*et cetera*)	etc.
Angstrom (unit)	A
anno Domini	A.D.
ante meridiem (before noon)	AM
antilogarithm	antilog
aperture ratio 16	*f*/16
approximate (as adj) (or use "about")	approx
aqueous	aq
are (100 m²)	*spell out*
as desired (*ad libitum*)	ad lib.
atmosphere(s)	atm
atomic weight	at. wt.
atto (prefix, 10^{-18})	a
audio-frequency (adj)	af
average (abbreviate in equations and tables only)	avg
avoirdupois	avdp

B

barrel(s)	bl
basal metabolic rate	BMR

* (Spectrophotometric unit equal to $\log_{10} (1/T)$ or $\log_{10} (I_o/I)$ where T = transmittancy, I_o = intensity of radiation entering medium, and I = intensity after traversing the medium. Transmittancy refers to the properties of the solute, the optical properties of the cuvette and solvent having been eliminated by suitable control. Transmittance and absorbance refer to the optical properties of the entire assembly of cuvette, solvent, and solute.) *See also* molecular extinction coefficient.

Baumé (with numeral, omit
  degree symbol)   Bé
before noon (*ante meridiem*)   AM
billion, *see* **giga**
billion electron volts   **Gev**
biochemical oxygen demand   BOD
body weight   body wt
boiling point   bp
British antilewisite (2,3-
  dimercapto-1-propanol)   BAL
British thermal unit(s)   BTU
bushel(s)   bu

c

calorie(s) (small, gram-
  calorie)   cal
Calorie(s) (large, kilogram
  calorie)   kcal
Celsius (with numeral, omit
  degree symbol)   C
cent   *spell out*
centi (prefix, 10^{-2})   c
centigrade, *see* Celsius
centigram(s)   cg
centimeter(s)   cm
centimeter, square cm^2
centimeter-gram-second
  (system)   cgs
central nervous system   CNS
chemically pure   cp
circa (about)   ca.

coefficient   coef
coenzyme A   CoA
coenzyme A and its acyl
  derivatives   Acyl-CoA
compare (*conferre*) (avoid
  use of abbreviation if *see* is
  meant)   cf.
concentrate   conc
concentrated   concd
concentration   concn
conductivity   cond
configuration*   D-, L-, DL-
constant   const
corrected (of melting
  points)   cor
cosine   cos
coulomb   coul
counts per minute   count/min
counts per second   count/sec
crossed with (genetics)   ×
cubic centimeter(s) cm^3, cc
cubic foot (feet) ft^3
cubic kilometers km^3
cubic meter(s) m^3
cubic micron(s) μ^3
cubic millimeter(s) mm^3
cubic yard(s) yd^3
curie (3.7 × 10^{10} disinte-
  gration/sec)   c
cycles per minute   cycle/min
cycles per second   cycle/sec

---

* Use small capital letters only for optically active compounds and their racemic forms when the compounds (carbohydrates, amino acids, and a few other substances) can be correlated sterically with glyceraldehyde or serine. In other cases *d-*, and *l-*, *dextro-* and *levo-*, or (+)- and (—)- are used to denote direction of optical rotation. Racemic compounds are designated by *dl-*, (±)-, or the italicized word *inactive-* (as *inactive-*galactose). DL- is used only when the prefix D- or L- can be properly applied in naming the optically active isomer.

D

day	*spell out*
DDT, *see* ethane	
deci (prefix, 10^{-1})	d
decibel	db
decigram (0.1 g)	dg
decimeter (0.1 m)	dm
decompose (melting point)	decomp, dec
degree, Celsius (omit degree symbol)	C
degree, Fahrenheit (omit degree symbol)	F
degree, Kelvin (omit degree symbol)	K
degree (space)	deg or °
degrees of freedom (statistics)	df (in tables)
deka (prefix, 10)	dk
density (*as* d_{13}: specific gravity at 13 C referred to water at 4 C; d_{20}^{20} at 20 C referred to water at same temperature)	d
deoxyribonuclease	*spell out*
deoxyribonucleic acid	DNA
dextrorotatory (*see* configuration)	*d-, dextro-*, (+)-
diameter	diam
2,4-dichlorophenoxyacetic acid	2,4-D
diffusion coefficient (usually given in cm^2/sec)	$D, D_{20,\ w}$
diphosphopyridine nucleotide, *see* nicotinamide	
direct current (adj)	d-c
disintegration per minute	dpm
disintegration per second	dps
dissociation constant, negative log of	pK'
dollar	*spell out* or $ with numerals
dozen	doz
dram	dr
dry weight	dry wt

E

east	E
effective dose, median	ED_{50}
electrocardiogram	ECG
electrode potential	E
electrode potential, standard	E_0
electrode potential, standard at constant pH	E'_0
electroencephalogram	EEG
electromotive force	emf
electromyogram	EMG
electron paramagnetic resonance	EPR
electron volt(s)	ev
erg	*spell out*
et alibi (and elsewhere); *et alii* (and others)	et al.
et cetera (and the rest)	etc.
ethane, 1,1,1-trichloro-2,2-bis(*p*-chlorophenyl)-	DDT
ethylenediaminetetraacetate	EDTA (*not* Versene)
exempli gratia (for example)	e.g.
extinction ($\log I_0/I$)	E

F

Fahrenheit (with numeral, omit degree symbol)	F

farad	*spell out*
female	♀
femto (prefix, 10^{-15})	f
figure(s) (illustration)	Fig.
filial generations (genetics)	F_1, F_2, F_3, etc.
flavin adenine dinucleotide and its reduced form	FAD FADH$_2$
flavin mononucleotide and its reduced form	FMN FMNH$_2$
focal length	$f/$
foot *or* feet	ft
foot candle	ft-c
for example (*exempli gratia*)	e.g.
forenoon	AM
forma (taxonomy only)	f.
freezing point	fp
frequency modulation	FM
fusion point (*see* mp)	fup

G

gallon(s)	gal
gamma (*see* microgram)	
generations, filial (genetics)	F_1, F_2, F_3, etc.
genus, new	gen. n.
giga (prefix, 10^9)	G
glutathione, oxidized	GSSG
glutathione, reduced	GSH
grain(s)	gr
gram(s)	g
gram calorie	cal
gram molecule	g mole (*or* mole)
gravity, centrifugal	g

H

hecto (prefix, 10^2)	h
hectometer (100 m)	hm
hemoglobin (*thus*, HbO$_2$, oxygenated hemoglobin)	Hb
horsepower	hp
hour(s)	hr
hundredweight	cwt
hydrogen ion concentration, negative log of;	pH
plural	pH values

I

ibidem (in the same place)	ibid.
id est (that is)	i.e.
inch(es)	*spell out*
infective dose, median (infect 50% of inoculated group)	ID$_{50}$
infrared	IR (in tables)
international unit	IU
intracutaneous	ic
intramuscular, intramuscularly	im
intraperitoneal, intraperitoneally	ip
intravenous, intravenously (do not confuse with Roman IV)	iv

K

Kelvin (scale in which zero is -273.1 C) (with numeral, omit degree symbol)	K
kilo (prefix, 10^3)	k
kilocalorie(s)	kcal

kilocycle(s)	kc
kilocycles per second	kc/sec
kiloelectron volt	kev
kilogram(s)	kg
kiloliter(s)	kliter
kilometer(s)	km
kiloröntgen(s)	kr
kilovolt(s)	kv
kilowatt(s)	kw

L

lambda, *see* microliter	
Lambert	**L**
latitude	lat
lethal dose, median (lethal for 50% of inoculated group)	LD$_{50}$
levorotatory (*see also* configuration)	*l-, levo-, (-)-*
liter(s)	*spell out*
loco citato (in the place cited), *avoid use*	loc. cit.
logarithm (common, base 10) *in formulas*	log, log$_{10}$
logarithm (natural base e) *in formulas*	ln, log$_e$
longitude	long

M

magnified by	×
male	♂
maximum	max
mega (prefix 10^6)	M
melting point	mp
metabolic rate	MR
meter(s)	m

meter(s), cubic	m^3
meter(s), square	m^2
methemoglobin	MetHb
mho (reciprocal ohm)	*spell out*
micro (prefix, 10^{-6})	μ
microcurie(s)	μc
microfarad	μf
microgram (do not use gamma, γ)	μg
microliter (do not use lambda, λ)	μliter
micromicron (10^{-9} mm)	$\mu\mu$ *or* pm
micromolar (unit of concn)	μM
micromole (unit of mass)	μmole
micron(s) (10^{-3} mm)	μ
microvolt	μv
microwatt	μw
mile(s)	*spell out*
miles per hour	mph
milli (prefix, 10^{-3})	m
milliampere(s)	ma
millicurie(s)	mc
milliequivalent(s)	meq, mEq
milligram(s)	mg
milligrams per cent (mg%, *never use*, see p. 33)	
milliliter(s)	ml
millimeter(s)	mm
millimeter(s), square	mm^2
millimicrogram	mμg *or* ng
millimicron (10^{-6} mm)	mμ
millimolar (unit of concn)	mM
millimole (unit of mass)	mmole
million electron volts	Mev
milliosmols	*spell out*
millivolt(s)	mv
millivolt-second	mv-sec
minimum *or* minute(s)	min

minimum lethal dose (do not
 use for lethal dose, median) MLD

minute(s) or minimum   min

minute (angular measure)   ′

molar (mole per liter)   M

mole (a gram molecule)   mole

molecular extinction coefficient
 ($\varepsilon = AM/bc$ where A is
 absorbancy, M is molecular
 weight, b is cell length in
 centimeters, and c the concentration in grams per liter) ε

molecular weight   mol wt

month   *spell out*

morning (*ante meridiem*)   AM

myria (prefix, 10^4)   my

N

nano (prefix, 10^{-9})   n

new genus   **gen. n.**

new species   sp. n.

nicotinamide mononucleo-
 tide   NMN

nicotinamide adenine
 dinucleotide   NAD *or* NAD⁺
     (formerly DPN, CoI)

nicotinamide adenine
 dinucleotide, reduced
 form   NADH

nicotinamide adenine
 dinucleotide
 phosphate   NADP *or* NADP⁺
     (formerly TPN, CoII)

nicotinamide adenine
 dinucleotide phosphate,
 reduced form   NADPH

nonprotein nitrogen   NPN

noon (*meridianus*)   M

normal (concn, 0.1 N)   N

normal (in trivial names
 of organic compounds)   *n-*

normal temperature and
 pressure   NTP

north, northwest   N, NW

nuclear magnetic resonance   n.m.r.

number (*numero*) in
 enumeration   no.

numerical aperture (in
 microscopy)   NA

O

ohm   *spell out*

opere citato (in the work
 cited), *avoid use*   op. cit.

optical density   OD

optical rotation
 Specific optical rotation
 (with concn %, w/v), thus,
 $[\alpha]^{20}_{D}$, $[\alpha]^{25}_{5461}$, etc.
 Molecular optical rotation
 ($=[\alpha] \times \text{mol wt}/10$), thus,
 $[M]^{20}_{D}$, $[M]^{25}_{5461}$, etc.

optimal (adj), optimum
 (noun)   opt

osmol   *spell out*

ounce   oz

oxyhemoglobin HbO_2

P

page(s)   p.

paralysis, median PD_{50}

parts per million   ppm

per cent   %

per thousand, per mil	$^{0}/_{00}$
pico (prefix, 10^{-12})	p
post meridiem (afternoon)	PM
precipitate (in tables)	ppt
preparation (in tables)	prepn
probability (that an event is due to chance alone)	*P*
pounds(s) (*libra*)	lb.
pounds per square inch	lb/in², psi

Q

qualitative	qual (in tables)
quantitative	quant (in tables)

R

radiation, ionizing, absorbed dose (100 ergs/g of irradiated material). Use in place of (rep) röntgen equivalent physical	rad
radiation, relative biological effectiveness (one type of radiation compared to another)	RBE
radio-frequency	rf
red blood cells	RBC
refractive index (at stated temperature and wavelength, thus, $[n]^{20}_{D}$ for 20 C and sodium light)	*n*
relative humidity	*spell out*
respiratory quotient	RQ
reticuloendothelial system	RES

revolutions per minute (*use g where possible*)	rpm, rev/min
ribonuclease (enzyme)	*spell out*
ribonucleic acid	RNA
röntgen (unit of exposure dose of X- or γ-radiation)	r
röntgen equivalent man (rad × RBE = rem)	rem

S

salinity (per thousand, per mil)	$^{0}/_{00}$
second(s) (time)	sec
second(s) (angular measure)	″
sedimentation coefficient corrected to 20 C in water. (S_{20} may be used if not ambiguous)	$S_{20, w}$
see (do not use cf.)	*spell out*
sine	sin
south, southwest	S, SW
species (taxonomy only)	sp.
species, new	sp. n.
specific gravity	sp gr
spectrophotometric units, *see* absorbancy *and* molecular extinction coefficient	
square	sq
square centimeter	cm²
square foot	ft²
square meter	m²
square millimeter	mm²
standard deviation	SD
standard error	SE
sulfhydryl *or* thiol group	SH⁻

T

tangent	tan
temperature	temp
tera (prefix, 10^{12})	T
that is (*id est*)	i.e.
ton	*spell out*
(*or* T with numerals)	
trichloroacetic acid (TCA is not acceptable)	*spell out*
1,1,1,trichloro-2,2,-di-(*p*-chlorophenyl)-ethane	DDT
triphosphopyridine nucleotide, *see* nicotinamide	
tris buffer (give chemical name when first mentioned) [tris (hydroxymethyl) amino methane *or* 2-amino-2-(hydroxymethyl)-1,3-propanediol]	Tris

U

ultraviolet (with numeral in tables)	UV
uncorrected (of melting points)	unc

V

variety(ies) (in taxonomy only)	var.
versus (against)	vs.

viscosity etc.

viscosity (symbol, eta)	η
volt	v
volume (with numeral in tables)	vol
volume/volume (concn)	v/v

W

watt	w
wavelength (symbol, lambda)	λ
week(s)	*spell out*
(*or* wk with numeral in table)	
weight	wt
weight/volume (concn)	w/v
(specify units of measure)	
west	W

X

X-irradiation

X-ray (adj and noun)

Y

yard(s)	*spell out*
(*or* yd with numeral in tables)	
year(s)	*spell out*
(*or* yr with numeral in tables)	

GREEK ALPHABET Greek letters are frequently used as symbols and in mathematical formulas. They should be clearly drawn by hand if not available on the typewriter. To prevent confusion spell them out in the margin. Since the capital Greek letters A, B, E, Z, H, I, K, M, N, O, P, T, and X are identical with certain English letters, avoid them as symbols.

Name of Letter	Capital	Small	Latin and English Equivalent
alpha	A	α	a
beta	B	β	b
gamma	Γ	γ	g (or n)
delta	Δ	δ	d
epsilon	E	ε	e
zeta	Z	ζ	z
eta	H	η	ē
theta	Θ	θ	th (or t)
iota	I	ι	i
kappa	K	κ	c (or k)
lambda	Λ	λ	l
mu	M	μ	m
nu	N	ν	n
xi	Ξ	ξ	x
omicron	O	o	o
pi	Π	π	p
rho	P	ρ	r (or rh)
sigma	Σ	σ, ς	s
tau	T	τ	t
upsilon	Υ	υ	y (or u)
phi	Φ	ϕ	ph (or f)
chi	X	χ	ch
psi	Ψ	ψ	ps
omega	Ω	ω	ō

RUSSIAN ALPHABET   Russian uses the Cyrillic, derived from the Greek, alphabet. Several systems of transliteration are used in English-speaking countries; the one used below is recommended until full agreement is reached.

Draft Table for Modern Russian Letters

British Standards Institution—

American Standards Association Sectional Committee Z 39

Russian	BSI	BSI-ASA/SC-Z39	Russian	BSI	BSI-ASA/SC-Z39
1 А а	a	a	17 Р р	r	r
2 Б б	b	b	18 С с	s	s
3 В в	v	v	19 Т т	t	t[footnote (1)]
4 Г г	g	g	20 У у	u	u
5 Д д	d	d	21 Ф ф	f	f
6 Е е	e	e	22 Х х	kh	kh
7 Ж ж	zh	zh	23 Ц ц	ts	ts
8 З з	z	z	24 Ч ч	ch	ch
9 И и	i	i	25 Ш ш	sh	sh[footnote (2)]
10 Й й	ï	ï	26 Щ щ	shch	shch
11 К к	k	k	27 Ъ ъ	ʼʼ	ʼʼ
12 Л л	l	l	28 Ы ы	ȳ	y[footnote (3)]
13 М м	m	m	29 Ь ь	ʼ	ʼ
14 Н н	n	n	30 Э э	é	ē
15 О о	o	o	31 Ю ю	yu	yu
16 П п	p	p	32 Я я	ya	ya

(1) Use t• when т (No. 19) is followed by с (No. 18)

(2) Use sh• when ш (No. 25) is followed by ч (No. 24)

(3) ȳ (with a bar) may be used optionally when followed by а (No. 1) or у (No. 20)

DIACRITICAL MARKS   Diacritical marks distinguish letters phonetically. Use the following as they are in the language of the country of origin:

Mark	Name	Example
Å	circled *or* ringed A	Ångstrom
´	acute accent	beauté
`	grave	le congrès
¸	cedilla	garçon
͑	inverted cedilla	Dąbrowa
ˆ	circumflex	bâtir
ˇ	inverted circumflex	Čechoslovaca
¨	dieresis	preëminence
˘	kratkaya *or* breve	Omskiĭ
¯	macron	Kyūshū
ʼ	soft sign	Krasil'nikov
/	slash *or* stod	København
⁄	stroke	społka
˙	superior dot	Skarżysko
~	tilde	Español
¨ *or* ''	umlaut	für Anfänger

Many printers do not have type for all these marks and substitutes may be necessary. Thus, the dieresis is commonly used for the umlaut and the stod. Diacritical marks are not commonly used in anglicized words of foreign origin or in place names of foreign origin when applied to places in the United States.

2. Preparation of Copy

Before the final draft of your manuscript is typed, examine a recent issue of the journal in which you propose to publish. Read the "Instructions to Authors" or similar material, which appears in most journals. Edit your rough draft to conform in all details with these instructions. Point out to the typist all matters, even the seemingly trivial, where her habitual ways differ from the style acceptable to the journal. The time you spend on these matters may save weeks of delay in publication. Remember that someone must find and correct the errors before your paper is printed; that someone should be you.

Paper Use white paper, $8\frac{1}{2} \times 11$ inches or $8 \times 10\frac{1}{2}$ inches, neither glazed nor too rough for erasures and corrections in ink. For the ribbon copy use 16-pound bond with rag content; for the carbons use 13-pound bond or other thin paper of good quality.

Typing Keep type faces clean with a brush. Use a black ribbon neither so worn that the typing is faint nor so new that the impression smears. Discard carbon paper before it fails to make legible copies.

Type on one side of the paper only, keep lines fairly uniform in length, and leave margins of 1 to 1½ inches for the editor's marks and queries. Avoid dividing a word at the end of a line.

Double-space text, quotations, footnotes, tables and table headings, legends, and references to literature. Use even greater spacing around equations and formulas. This space is essential to the editor for marking copy and to the printer for ease and accuracy in composition.

Make at least two carbon copies corresponding in paging and in all insertions and corrections. Submit one carbon copy with the original to expedite editorial review. Keep one copy of the manuscript.

Start a new page for each section, and arrange the copy in the following order: (i) title, by-line, running head, name and address for mailing; (ii) abstract; (iii) text, in the natural sequence of its parts; (iv) acknowledgments; (v) references to literature; (vi) footnotes; (vii) tables; (viii) legends for figures; and (ix) the figures. If the journal to which you submit the manuscript does not publish an abstract with the paper, include one on an unnumbered page for *Biological Abstracts*.

Check the entire manuscript for typographical errors, paying particular attention to quotations, citations, technical terms, and names of persons and places. Check the list of references against original sources for (i) wording, (ii) spelling, (iii) capitalization, (iv) italics, (v) diacritical marks, (vi) abbreviations, (vii) page and volume numbers and dates. Then collate the references in the text with this verified list. After final typing, check the numerical data in the text and tables.

Paging Number all pages consecutively in the upper right-hand corner. Never use a number and letter (e.g., 3A, 3B) for pages you insert without noting insertion (3A follows, 3B precedes) on pages immediately preceding and following; otherwise such pages may be lost without indication that they are missing. Never staple or bind the manuscript.

Corrections and Insertions Type brief corrections, or print them legibly, above the line concerned, and show with a caret (∧) the exact place for the insertion. Do not write in margins or below the line. Do not attach slips of paper (flyers) to the pages. Retype any page needing lengthy insertions. If the retyping results in a page only partly filled, draw a diagonal line below the text to indicate that additional material follows. If you insert pages, number them as recommended under Paging above.

Title   Phrase the title to identify the content of the article. Where appropriate, include the nature of the study, the experimental organism used, the place of field study, and the technical approach (morphology, histochemistry, demography, etc.). Make the title short, specific, and informative. Clarity and conciseness are essential for indexing, abstracting, and retrieval (*see also* Abstract, p. 49).

Some primary journals permit no more than 90 characters and spaces; others, no more than 10 words. Avoid unnecessary *the*'s and redundant openings such as *Investigations on, The nature of, Studies of,* and *Contributions to.* Do not identify a publication as number one of a series unless a second paper is assured of publication.

The following editorial from *Biological Abstracts* [volume 36(9), 1 May 1961] explains the importance of a title:

To your paper, its title may mean the difference between recognition and oblivion. The scientific literature is already so voluminous that you—if you follow the behavior pattern of most of your colleagues—consider yourself fortunate when you can find time to scan only the titles of abstracts in selected subject areas of interest. Once you locate a clue to something important in the title of a paper, you may then read the abstract, or perhaps go directly to the source of the publication. Admittedly, by this method of search for information you will have passed up papers of significance to your work, if nothing in their titles attracted you to dig deeper.

Titles assume even greater importance when we turn over responsibility for searching them to mechanical devices. In filling the need for specific information we are having to rely ever more heavily on the machine for quick access to a mass of relatively unclassified literature—one rapid way, already in use, is to search mechanically only titles of papers, to locate significant or "key" words. Under such a scheme, a paper improperly titled may be lost for some time, if not forever.

In a very real sense, you are providing the first index to your paper when you construct its title, and your skill in doing so may affect seriously the availability to science of the contribution your work represents. Consider, for example, the difference in the informative properties of the following, actual titles of abstracts chosen at random from a past issue of *Biological Abstracts*: (1) "Small-cell malignant lesions of the thyroid gland"; and (2) "In vitro effects of steroids upon electrolyte transfer through frog skin." In the first instance one can only guess as to what organism was involved, what type of study or approach the author made, or what aspect of malignancy or thyroid involvement he investigated; whereas the specific information contained in the second title gives it obvious advantages—to the human reader, also to the machine.

When you write your next paper, why not keep in mind that more people will encounter its title than any other part? Take care to make that title specific, informative, so that it will serve as an accurate guide to the work you are reporting. The contribution that is lost to science, or comes too late, represents a tragic waste of human resources. We sincerely believe that you have a responsibility to neglect no detail that will help insure the availability, hence the value, of the results of your scientific efforts.

By-Line

The by-line comprises two elements: name of the author(s) and of the institution(s) where the investigation was made. Type your name as you customarily write it. To avoid confusion in the literature, use this form consistently. Omit titles and degrees. Give the name of your department and institution, and spell out the names of the city and state. When co-authors represent different institutions, name the authors and their institutions in order, thus:

J. Quentin Doe and R. U. Shure

Department of Biology, Blank College, Pine City, Illinois

and

Department of Zoology, Red Brick University, Bearbute, Alaska

Naming an institution in the by-line implies that the research was done there. If the research was conducted in two places, name both. If you change institutions, do not credit the new one for work done at the old.

Be sure to include the address to which editorial correspondence and galley proof should be sent, as well as requests for reprints.

It is unethical to include in the by-line the name of any person who was not actually engaged in the reported research. This breach of ethics is usually committed by an institutional superior who insists that his name appear.

If your article is based upon a dissertation or thesis, so identify it in a footnote in the form prescribed by the institution.

Running Head

Supply a running head to be set at the top of each right-hand page of the printed article. This is usually a shortened title of at most 40 characters and spaces and need be only a key phrase identified with the main title. The running head for a paper entitled: "Morphological differentiation and adaptation in the Galápagos finches" might be "Galápagos finches."

Abstract The abstract summarizes the contents and conclusions of the paper, points out new information in the paper, and indicates the relevance of the work. It serves two functions: when accompanying the complete article, it is a useful preview; published alone, it provides for wide acquaintance with the work and with its source.

State briefly and specifically what the paper reports. Do not describe the paper in such terms as "Feeding activity of fish during the summer months is discussed," or "Feeding activity of fish during the summer months was observed." Write instead "In the summer largemouth bass fed most actively between 9:30 and 11:30 A M"

The term "synopsis" has been adopted by the Royal Society of London and by the UNESCO International Conference on Science Abstracting, 1949, to describe an author's abstract published with the paper. A summary of the recommendations of the International Council of Scientific Unions Abstracting Board, and the Subcommittee on Abstracts of the American Standards Association, follows.

STYLE The abstract should be completely self-explanatory and intelligible in itself. Assume that your readers have some knowledge of the subject, but have not read the paper. Use complete sentences (instead of a mere list of headings) and avoid jargon. Use standard scientific nomenclature rather than proprietary terms. Do not use abbreviations in the title or the abstract (*see also* p. 47). Avoid abbreviations in the text, except those in international usage (e.g., units of weight and measurement).

CONTENT Indicate the objective and topics covered. State the methods. For new methods, give the basic principle, range of operation, and degree of accuracy. Omit references to literature, illustrations, and tables. Call attention to names of new compounds, minerals, species, etc., to new numerical data, such as physical constants and statistical results, and to new items and observations, even though some may be incidental. Keep the abstract to 200 words or to the length specified by the journal.

Preparing the abstract:

1) If the journal to which you are submitting the manuscript publishes abstracts, include the abstract with the manuscript. A copy of the journal or of page proof will be sent to *Biological Abstracts*.

2) If the journal does not publish abstracts, type an abstract separately, headed by the name(s) of the author(s) and the address (in parentheses), the title of the article, and the journal name (leave space for volume, pages, and year) :

SMITH, A. B. (Univ. Hawaii, Honolulu) , and W. KARAKAWA. Metabolism of phosphorus in sugar cane. Amer. J. Bot. . . . — (Text of Abstract)

The editor will complete the citation and will send the copy to *Biological Abstracts.*

INDEX WORDS Select as many as 10 words essential for indexing your paper and place them at the bottom of the abstract.

Headings Headings point up for the reader the organization of the text. They also serve as an outline for the writer. After the **Abstract** and introductory statements, the main divisions of the article need principal headings, for example:

Materials and Methods, for the general source of items and the techniques used.

Results, for the observations and data (but not a discussion of the literature).

Discussion, for connecting new findings with previous studies, and for interpretations.

Literature Cited, for only those publications mentioned in the text.

Subheadings of lower rank may be desirable in a long article but should be used sparingly.

Illustrations and Legends Many articles need illustrations. All illustrations should be functional; none should repeat material presented in tables or text. Black-and-white drawings, graphs, and maps are reproduced as zinc engravings and printed as line cuts. Photographs and tone drawings may be reproduced as copper engravings and printed as halftones. Illustrations are generally called "figures"; the designation "plates" is falling into disuse. Illustrations are expensive; be certain yours are essential. If you have color illustrations, consult the editor about feasibility and costs before submitting them.

Distinguish carefully between an illustration suitable for a slide to be projected in a lecture and one, especially a graph which gives quantitative data, suitable for the permanent record. The slide must include lettering to designate the curves and some information on their meaning. Rough plotting and smoothed curves are frequently all that is necessary. But the permanent record of your measurements must be accurately plotted, all points being shown by suitable symbols (*see* p. 54). Where the points represent the means of a suitable number of observations, indicate the magnitude of the standard error by vertical lines centered at the points. The ordinates both at the left and the right, as well as the abscissa, must have index marks so that your data can be recovered with moderate accuracy by use of a ruler. Use only essential labels on the drawing, supplementing them as necessary in the legend. In giving units of measure follow the principles given on pages 57 and 58.

Make black-and-white drawings with India ink on pure white stock or tracing paper; fuzzy lines and shades of gray will not reproduce clearly. Printed transparent overlays with patterns of lines, dots, stippling, or cross-hatching are available commercially for different degrees of reduction. If these are needed, mount them so that the pattern does not obscure printing or other critical material underneath. Be sure that the overlay is attached securely everywhere, with no air bubbles beneath. Draw graphs on coordinate paper printed in pale blue so that the grid will not reproduce. Orange, yellow, green, and red grids reproduce as black.

Strive for technical perfection in the original art work. Faults in the original are often accentuated in the printed reproduction. Use compass or squares to draw the symbols for the points of observation (see p. 54), and scrolls to draw the curves. Mechanical aids are available for drawing the lettering. Make sure that rectangular illustrations are geometrically true; arrange drawings to utilize a block of page space economically, either in one or two columns of print, in keeping with the format of the journal in which you wish to publish. For the reader's convenience, arrange all lettering to be read from one position. For many helpful suggestions see the American Standards Association *Illustrations for Publication and Projection* (Bulletin Y15.1–1959), and the references (p. 106).

Art work submitted with the manuscript ordinarily should be $8\frac{1}{2} \times 11$ inches or smaller. Many illustrations benefit from some degree of reduction. Plan line drawings for reduction of 50% or more; this will minimize flaws. Remember that not only the over-all dimensions but also the thickness of individual lines, spaces, and letters will be reduced proportionally. A reducing lens is helpful for inspecting a figure during preparation. Fig. 1

ABCDEFGHIJKLMNOPQRSTUVWXYZ
1234567890

ABCDEFGHIJKLMNOPQRSTUVWXYZ

ABCDEFGH ABCDEFGH ABCDEFGH

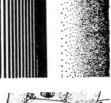

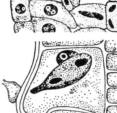

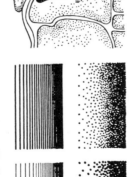

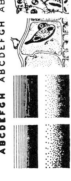

ABCDEFGHIJKLMNOPQRSTUVWXYZ

ABCDEFGHIJKLMNOPQRSTUVWXYZ
1234567890

ABCDEFGHIJKLMNOPQRSTUVWXYZ

ABCDEFGH ABCDEFGH ABCDEFGH

ABCDEFGHIJKLMNOPQRSTUVWXYZ
1234567890
ABCDEFGHIJKLMNOPQRSTUVWXYZ
ABCDEFGH ABCDEFGH ABCDEFGH

FIG. 1. Letters, lines and dots in relation to reduction for the printed page. Top—original size. Lower left—½ size. Lower right—¼ size. Thin black lines hold up well, but small black dots and white spaces between black lines or dots may be lost. Delicate shading may be obtained if it is kept rather open, and if the size and spacing of the dots are adjusted to the amount of reduction from the original. Reprinted by permission of Riker and Riker.

shows the effect of reduction on various patterns and letters. Where necessary, indicate a linear scale on the figure itself, or state the magnification on the legend. Provide a micron scale directly on the micrographs. You are responsible for seeing that the magnification reported corresponds with the final reproduction. On maps, include a scale of distance and a directional indication and marginal indications of latitude and longitude.

When scaling illustrations for reproduction to proper size, you can use the simple equation:

$$\frac{\text{Reduced width}}{\text{Original width}} \times \text{original height} = \text{reduced height}$$

A geometrical method for sizing illustrations is shown in Fig. 2. On a piece of paper the size $(ABCD)$ of the original illustration draw a diagonal line AC. Measure along the top the desired width (AE) of the cut and draw a perpendicular line (EF). The line EF gives the length of the reduced cut.

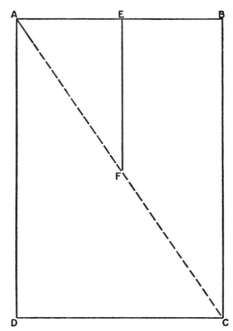

FIG. 2. *A method for scaling illustrations.*

This method can be used to determine the reduction necessary to fit an illustration into a given space.

Submit the original line drawings or equally good glossy prints, with extra copies for the reviewers if required by the journal. *Never submit a map or illustration so large that it must be sent in a mailing tube or separate package;* have it reduced by photography and send a print with the manuscript.

Photographs for publication need high contrast and must be printed on glossy paper. A size of about 5×7 inches is usually adequate. If you do not trim ("crop") distracting or nonessential features of the photograph, outline the essential features on a transparent overlay. Mark each photograph *lightly* in soft pencil on the margin (front or back), with figure number, author's name, and if desirable the magnification of the print. Identify the top. Take care that no grooves, gouges, or creases appear on the face; never use paper clips on a glossy print or write so firmly on the back that the face is damaged. Several photographs can frequently be combined into a single illustration, with one legend explaining the figures, each designated by a letter or number. Some journals require unmounted original prints. If your journal requires mounted prints, trim them square, align them neatly, and affix with adhesive on white mounting board. Ship photographs flat (never rolled or folded); protect them with stout cardboard backing and a durable envelope or commercial mailer.

Cite all illustrations in the text (as Fig. X), numbering them in one consecutive series. A circled note in the margin, as here shown, enables the editor or printer to place the figure correctly in the text.

Type titles (underline for italics) and legends for illustrations double spaced, grouped separately from the text; do not attach them to the art work. Legends should be concise and yet clearly explain the figures. Symbols and explanations may appear directly on the figures if space permits. If an explanatory key within a figure causes crowding, use a separate legend for such information. When symbols are explained in the legend, use only the following symbols for which printers have standard characters in type:

You are responsible for obtaining written permission to use copyrighted illustrations. Courtesy demands a credit line for any illustration not yours.

Tables   Tables may provide the most effective means for organizing numerical data, especially if extensive. They should make classification evident, facilitate comparisons, reveal relationships, and save space. A table should be self-explanatory. The data may be referred to and discussed, but not repeated extensively in the text. Where important, draw attention to trends. Organize the data to bring out pertinent comparisons clearly. Avoid presenting numerical data with the appearance of greater precision than accuracy of the methods justifies. As a rule only three significant figures are needed. Only work of the highest accuracy attainable by refined physical methods warrants more. Aside from statistics, tables that show five or more significant figures merely reflect on the good sense of the author. Do not include columns of data that can be calculated easily from data given in other columns.

The parts of a table are the *number* and *title*, on the same line; the *boxhead*, identifying the entries in the vertical columns; the *stub*, identifying the entries in the horizontal lines; the *field*, containing the data. Where the data report the results of experiments carried out under a fixed and repeated set of conditions, supply a caption under the title giving these conditions in precise detail.

Tables commonly have cross rules: a single rule below the title; a single rule below the boxhead; a single rule at the bottom (Table 4).

TABLE 4.   *Title* (Underline for italics)

Boxhead for Stub	Boxhead
Stub	Field

Because hand-set rules increase costs greatly, many journals use no vertical rules (Table 5) and a minimum of horizontal rules; a few journals use none. Additional rules (vertical or horizontal) may be needed if several subheads are used in the boxhead (Table 6).

Numerical data of equal length should be centered in the column. If entries are unequal, center the longest and align the rest on the decimal, or at the right or the left margin. Do not use minus sign and dash in the same column of numbers that show a range; instead substitute "to" for the dash.

TABLE 5.   *Occurrence of grasses of the tribe Hordeae in certain counties of Arizona**

County	Number of species of the genus		
	Hordeum	*Elymus†*	*Lolium*
Apache	2	7	0
Graham	1	7	1
Cochise	3	8	2

* Compiled from Gould, Frank W. 1951. Grasses of the Southwestern United States. Univ. Ariz. Bull. 22:1-343.

† Includes those species often segregated in the genus *Agropyron*.

TABLE 6.   *Temperature characteristics of various homeothermic animals*[a]

Animal	Rectal temperature, C			Critical air temperature,[b] C		Presence or absence of temperature regulating mechanism[c]			Thermo neutrality zone,[d] C
	Normal	Min	Max	Low	High	Sweat-ing	Shiv-ering	Pant-ing	
Man	37.0	22	44	17 to 22	32	+	+	0	23 to 34.5
Cat	37.2–39	17	42		32.2	0	+	+	10 to 30
Cow, dairy	38–39		42.8	−40	21–27	0		+	4.4 to 15.6
Dog	39.0	17	42.8	−40	29	0	+	+	−40 to 30
Elephant	35.9–36.7					0	+		
Guinea pig	38.5–39.9	21		−15	29.5			+	30 to 31
Chicken	40–42	25–27	45	−34	32.2	0	+	+	16 to 35

a Adapted from original table. Spector, W. S. (Ed.). 1956. *In* Handbook of biological data. W. B. Saunders Co., Philadelphia.

b Air temperature at which the first indication of change in rectal temperature occurs in the animal.

c Symbols: + = mechanism present; 0 = mechanism absent.

d Range of air temperature over which the metabolic rate is lowest and constant in the animal.

Align data with standard deviations first on the ±, then on the decimal points to the left and right:

60	60.5	54,321	37.5	23 to 34.5	22.3 ± 1.5
40	125.3	4,321	37.2-39	−20.8 to −10	847 ± 51
88	49.9	321	38-39	− 8 to 12	8.32 ± 0.12
57	0.5	21	35.9-36.7	− 1.7 to 2.8	0.64 ± 0.01

Determine the significant number of digits, and do not give percentages to more than one decimal (20.2%) unless extreme precision is both possible and essential.

Do not use a minus sign or dash for entries in the field of a table to indicate the lack of observations or tests. Avoid misalignment in typing columns and rows.

| *Set:* | aedf | ghkt
pdq
sos | axy
zdb
123
xyz | *Not:* | aedf | ghkt
pdq
sos | axy
zdb
123
xyz |

Symbols and common abbreviations may be used in large tables to save space. Footnotes to tables are frequently necessary. They should immediately follow the table, with each treated as a paragraph and referred to with a superscript letter (or symbol: * † ‡ §).

HEADINGS OF COLUMNS OF DATA

Where data are expressed in inconveniently large or small numbers, it is often best to indicate in the heading that all entries contain a common factor, e.g., 10^3 or 10^{-3}. Unfortunately, two conventions are in use. In one, the factor indicates that the data *have been multiplied* by the factor given. In the other, the factor indicates that the data *are to be multiplied* by the factor. Authors who use the first method will give 120 grams as 1.2 under the heading g × 10^{-2}, and those who use the second will give 1.2 under the heading g × 10^2. A reader who uses the first method will interpret g × 10^{-2} to mean 120 g and g × 10^2 to mean 0.012 g. A reader who uses the second method will make the opposite interpretations of the two forms. This is serious ambiguity. It can be resolved by associating the factor with the number rather than with the unit of measure. This convention requires that 120 grams be represented by 1.2 under the heading 10^2 g, and it conforms to the standard in which, for example, 1200 grams is represented by 1.2 under the heading kg, or 10^3 g.

Use special type styles, such as boldface and italic, only if essential in box-head, stub, and field—for example, italics for names of genera and species.

Plan tables to use space efficiently, and to fit either single- or multiple-column formats in the journal to which the manuscript is to be submitted. Large tables are costly and few journals will accept those requiring fold-out pages.

The manuscript of tables should be *double-spaced throughout,* including title, headings, and footnotes. Put each table on a separate sheet, cite it by number in the text, and indicate its approximate location by a circled marginal note (*see* p. 54).

Mathematical Formulas and Equations

Numbers, letters, and symbols in formulas and equations must be clear and accurate, and they must be in proper alignment. Allow extra space—triple or even quadruple—around typewritten equations. If your typewriter does not have special symbols, draw them neatly by hand. Note in pencil obscure modifications of symbols such as prime marks, dots over symbols, etc. Carefully distinguish the letter "O" from the number zero "0," the letter "l" from the number "1," the degree symbol from the superior letter "o" and the number "0." When the letter "x" is used to represent the multiplication sign ($\times$), indicate lightly in pencil "mult. sign." Draw Greek letters carefully, inserting marginal notation such as "Gk. beta" to avoid error. Encircle all marginal instructions not intended to be set in type.

Indicate type face by underlining as follows:

Roman capital letter, triple underline

Roman small capital, double underline

Boldface capital or lower case, wavy underline

Italic capital or lower case, single underline

Draw or type superior and inferior numbers, letters, and symbols (exponents or superscripts, and subscripts) in the proper position; if there is any doubt about the proper position, pencil a caret $\wedge$ over the characters to be set inferior and an inverted caret $\vee$ under the characters to be set superior. Use combinations of $\vee$ and $\wedge$ as necessary to mark inferiors to superiors (e x 2), inferiors to inferiors (e a 1), superiors to inferiors (e a 2), and superiors to superiors (e x 2).

Equations are extremely expensive to set in type, for they require much hand work, particularly when they contain built-up fractions, complicated exponents, radical signs, and symbols that occupy more than one line of type. Present your equations in the simplest form that can be obtained by ordinary mathematical manipulation: factoring, removing common factors, clearing fractions, etc. The following notations may be helpful; if you use them, the equations can be set in one line on a machine.

1) Use a case fraction instead of a built-up fraction:

$$\tfrac{1}{2}\,(a + b), \text{ not } \frac{a + b}{2} \tag{1}$$

2) Use a fractional exponent instead of a radical sign:

$$a\,(bc)^{1/2}, \text{ not } a\sqrt{bc} \tag{2}$$

3) Use the slant line (/) to avoid built-up fractions, taking care to insert the necessary parentheses:

$$x = (a + b)/(c + d), \text{ not } \frac{a + b}{c + d} \tag{3}$$

4) Use negative exponents when simplicity results:

$$a = \tfrac{2}{3}\,R^{-1}\,g\,\sin B, \text{ not } a = \frac{2\,g\,\sin B}{3R} \tag{4}$$

5) Avoid using a bar to mean average when more than one character is involved; instead, use pointed brackets with a subscript *avg*:

$$\langle a + b \rangle_{avg}, \text{ not } \overline{a + b} \tag{5}$$

6) When the argument of an exponential function is complicated, use the form "exp" and type the argument on the line instead of superior:

$$A \exp \tfrac{1}{2}\,(V/D), \text{ not } Ae^{\tfrac{1}{2}\,(V/D)} \tag{6}$$

7) Avoid aligning superiors directly over inferiors. The expression x_a^2 is fully as clear as $x{}_a^2$ and it can be set by machine. \qquad (7)

Draw complex equations in India ink on a separate page.

When equations are too complex for typing draw them in black ink on a separate page, and indicate their position in the text. When several equations are used, number them in parentheses at the right to permit reference to them in the text.

Statistics Statistical methods should be used in designing an experiment or a series of observations and in analyzing and interpreting quantitative data from a completed investigation. Since statistical methods are based on probability, they neither support poorly designed and inadequately controlled experiments nor prove the results beyond doubt.

In designing an experiment, keep in mind normal variations in biological materials, reliability of analytical methods, and errors arising from sampling. Use statistical methods to calculate how to extract the most information with the least experimentation. But statistics cannot substitute for thought and common sense, nor can common sense substitute for statistics.

When analyzing data, emphasize the biological results, not the statistical methods. A simple statement that the analyses yielded certain results usually justifies the interpretations and conclusions. Do not include unnecessary mathematical details. Do not report separate results from a large number of uniform or corresponding experiments, especially when analyzing the characteristics of a population. Adequate information is usually supplied by (i) the *number* (n) of individual observations; (ii) the *arithmetic mean* ($\bar{x}$); (iii) the *standard deviation* (SD, σ, or s_x) or *standard error* (SE). Such information may be included in text or table, as 321 ± 2.8 (7), where the numbers represent the mean $\pm$ SE or SD (indicate which) with the number of observations in parentheses. When reporting a difference between the means (or other statistics) of two groups of results, apply a test of significance or give the confidence limits. When representing statistical quantities by symbols, use Greek letters (Σ, ε, μ, etc.) for hypothetical characteristics of the population, and roman letters (S, s, m, etc.) for actual measurements based on samples from the population.

Omit long descriptions of statistical methods except in manuscripts dealing specifically with statistics, but cite the source of any unusual methods.

For details on the use of statistics in biology consult a good textbook, such as Bancroft (1959) or Bailey (1959).

Chemical Formulas and Equations

Chemical symbols and simple formulas may be used in text, tables, or figures as shorthand designations (Mg, Mn, HCl, CO_2, H_2SO_4, H_3PO_4, etc.). Ions may be indicated by adding symbols for the electrical charge (Mg^{2+}, SO_4^{2-} or SO_4'', H^+, Fe^{3+}, Cl^- or Cl', Na^+, etc.). The diatomic molecules of gases may also be denoted by their formulas (H_2, O_2, N_2, etc.).

When merely naming a salt, use its simplest formula (Na_2SO_4, KCl, $FeCl_3$, etc.) but when mentioning quantities of ordinarily hydrated salts, indicate the full molecular formula, for example: $BaCl_2 \cdot 2H_2O$, $Na_2SO_4 \cdot 10H_2O$, $K_4Fe(CN)_6 \cdot 3H_2O$. Avoid using a chemical symbol that can be mistaken for a word, particularly in beginning a sentence (*As* in these samples . . . . *He* was present in . . . . *I* was vaporized . . . .).

The formulas for simple organic substances may be used in the text if they save space, and if they can be printed in a single line (HCHO, CH_3COOH, C_6H_5OH). Avoid ambiguous formulas (C_2H_6O may be alcohol or acetone; $C_4H_4O_2$ could be any of at least eight substances). If possible, avoid formulas of substances with ring structures; they are difficult to set in type.

Where structures of organic substances are important, type or draw them carefully, centering them between lines of text and showing every significant detail clearly. Show only the more important chemical bonds by typing them as hyphens (the printer may substitute centered periods if space is limited); for example, leucine may be written

$$CH_3\text{-}CH(CH_3)\text{-}CH_2\text{-}CH(NH_2)\text{-}COOH$$

If all the bonds were indicated, the formula would occupy far more space and would be more difficult to comprehend at a glance. Avoid diagonal bond lines and diagonal arrows if possible.

If complex formulas are set by hand they occupy too much space. Accordingly, provide well-designed, black ink drawings suitable for reproduction by photoengraving. Indicate the exact position of each drawing in the text.

Isotopically labeled elements are indicated in American journals by the atomic weight of the isotope placed as a superior figure to the right of the symbol ($CH_3C^{14}OOH$ for acetic acid-1-C^{14}, $C^{14}H_3COOH$ for acetic acid-2-C^{14}). European journals place the atomic weight to the left and some American journals are conforming to this usage. When the name rather than the formula is used, place the symbol for the isotope after the name (leucine-N^{15}, thymidine-H^3). If the position of the labeled element is known, show this by a number before the symbol (sodium propionate-2-C^{14}); if unknown, or if the labeling is general, omit the number (glucose-C^{14}).

Center chemical equations between lines of text, and leave quadruple space above and below each. If equations represent an equilibrium, use the double arrow; if the reaction goes to completion, a single arrow. In presenting biochemical reactions authors frequently use the names of compounds rather than the complex formulas. Abbreviations may be used if generally understood. For example, a reaction catalyzed by an enzyme found in mammalian liver may be written:

$$\text{D-xylulose} + \text{ATP} \rightarrow \text{D-xylulose 5-phosphate} + \text{ADP}$$

In general, chemical equations, like mathematical equations, should balance. Where only an indication of the general course of a reaction influenced by a catalyst or specific reagent is necessary, diagrams like the following are appropriate:

ATP   phosphohexose

Glucose <———> glucose 6-phosphate <═════════> fructose 6-phosphate

isomerase

Descriptions of Solutions   Express the concentration of solutions in chemical terms, that is, either in normality (N) or molarity (M), and attach a number (1.0 N hydrochloric acid, *not* N hydrochloric acid).

Use the decimal system for fractional concentrations (0.1 N hydrochloric acid, *not* N/10 hydrochloric acid). Use only sufficient decimal places to indicate the accuracy with which the solution was prepared or standardized (0.502 N hydrochloric acid). For extremely dilute solutions, use the form 1.0×10^{-5} M, or 1.0×10^{-5} N, as the case may be. The chemical definition of concentration is preferred because expression as percentage is frequently ambiguous: 10% H_2SO_4 may mean 10 g of sulfuric acid (H_2SO_4 substance) in 100 ml of solution, or 10 ml of concentrated sulfuric acid (the commercial reagent which may be from 95 to 98% by weight or approximately 36 N) in 100 ml of solution; 10% sodium sulfate may be 0.07 M, 0.037 M, or 0.03 M, according to whether the anhydrous salt, the heptahydrate, or the decahydrate was weighed.

If you do use a percentage, specify the exact chemical substance weighed or measured, and whether by weight and volume (w/v) or by volume only (v/v). Dilutions of ethyl alcohol, for instance, are usually made from commercial alcohol of density 0.816, which has a concentration of 92.3% by weight and 94.9% by volume.

Sometimes special methods are used to prepare and describe solutions. A 1.0 molal solution contains 1.0 mole of the substance dissolved in 1,000 g of solvent. A 1.0 weight molar solution contains 1.0 mole of substance dissolved in sufficient water so that the solution weighs 1,000 g. Weight molar solutions are measured by weight.

Chemical Analyses and Physical Properties of Compounds

Give reference to all analytical or procedural methods not widely known. If you use an important modification of a fundamental method, state this (e.g., nitrogen was determined by the Kjeldahl method as modified by Hiller et al., 1948). Where the modification is trivial, cite only the fundamental publication. If your method is original, at least in part, describe it briefly, avoiding inconsequential details. The reader needs to know that a precipitate was centrifuged in the cold at $2,000 \times g$, but the make and type of centrifuge is usually unimportant. Since analytical chemists invariably use distilled or deionized water, this fact need not be mentioned unless specially purified water is essential. "The crystals were collected by filtration on a Büchner funnel, transferred to a weighing bottle, dried in a vacuum desiccator over phosphorus pentoxide, and weighed on an analytical balance" simply means that the crystals were filtered, dried in vacuo, and weighed; the rest is padding. Assume that the reader is technically competent.

Report analytical results in the following conventional form:

$$\text{Analysis: } C_{17}H_{20}N_4O_4; \text{ calculated: C, 59.29; H, 5.85; N, 16.27}$$
$$\text{found: C, 58.8; H, 6.03; N, 16.2}$$

Note the punctuation and the omission of the percentage symbol, and that the calculated values are given to four significant figures. The analytical results are given to only three figures, the last being adjusted. Only when extreme precautions are taken is a fourth figure justified.

Report the data on physical properties in the text in the following standard form, indicating special conditions of measurement:

Specific rotation: $[\alpha]_D^{22} = -20 \pm 2°$ (1.0 M in water)

Melting point: mp 140–142 C (unc), (cor), (copper block), (sealed tube)

Boiling point: bp 120 C at 15 mm

Specific refractive index: $[n]_\mathbf{D}^{16} = 1.4767$

Record temperature, wavelength of the light used in measuring specific rotation, the solvent, and concentration of the solute.

Statements of melting points should indicate whether you applied a correction for stem emergence of the thermometer. If no statement is made about technique, it is understood the substance was heated in an open tube immersed in a suitable bath. Avoid the ambiguous term *mixed melting point* by writing: mp 178–179 C (unc), and the mixture with an authentic sample of mp 179–180 C (unc) had a mp 177–179 C (unc). Boiling points are recorded at atmospheric pressure unless otherwise stated.

Chromatographic evidence for identity and purity is better presented by black ink tracing of the paper than by photographs. State the kind of paper, the solvent, the conditions, and the R_F values of all components present, together with those of authentic materials. Note that R_F means the ratio of the movement of the substance to that of the front, and that R is an italic capital and the $_F$ an inferior italic small capital (not lower case); also that the process is chromatography, the paper is a chromatogram. Avoid such neologisms as *papergram*. One does not *elute (or extract) the spots*, nor does one *extract the paper*; one elutes or extracts the substance from the paper. In column chromatography, one does not *pool the tubes,* or *titrate the tubes*; least of all does one *mix the tubes*, but the *fractions* or *contents* of the tubes.

Metabolic Quotients Suggestions for expressing metabolic quotients are

1) a) The symbol Q_x may represent metabolic quotients *only* in the units of microliters of gas X per milligram dry weight of biological material per hour.

   b) If the metabolite X is a solid or liquid, it is conventionally considered as a gas at normal temperature and pressure (NTP), 1 micromole of X being equivalent to 22.4 microliters.

2) Metabolic quotients in other units, such as micromoles of X per milligram dry weight per hour; microliters of X per milligram N per second, may be represented by the symbol q_x.

3) Define the units for Q or q clearly when first mentioned.

4) Indicate production and removal of metabolites by positive or negative quotients; omit the symbols (+ or −) if there is no confusion.
5) Indicate aerobic or anaerobic conditions thus:

$$Q_{CO_2}^{O_2} \qquad Q_{CO_2}^{N_2} \qquad q_{CO_2}^{O_2} \qquad q_{CO_2}^{N_2}$$

Measurements in another gas may be indicated thus: $Q_{CO_2}^{H_2}$

6) Indicate substrate in parentheses: $Q_{CO_2}^{N_2}$ (pyruvate)

7) You may omit the symbol Q_x or q_x, if you state the units (μmole : g wet weight : hour) whenever a quotient is mentioned.

Chemical Nomenclature

The index of *Chemical Abstracts* is the authority for the names of chemical compounds in the United States and Canada. Consult it in all doubtful cases. But many common names, not derived under the rules of chemical nomenclature, are current and useful: trivial and trade names (aspirin, cellophan, DDT, 2,4-D) and coinages to suggest chemical structure (methoxychlor). Trade names are officially registered and, if used, must be spelled and capitalized according to the owner's usage (Vaseline, Adrenalin). Use caution and common sense, following good usage in your field. A biochemist writing on mechanisms of respiration may properly use the name α-ketoglutaric acid, although *Chemical Abstracts* indexes this substance as 2-oxoglutaric acid. A plant pathologist may mention "nabam," which is indexed by *Chemical Abstracts* under this name, but with the instruction "*see* disodium salt under Carbamic acid, ethylenebis dithio-."

Many abbreviations for long complex names of organic compounds are current: NADP for nicotinamide-adenine dinucleotide phosphate, and EDTA for ethylenediaminetetraacetate. Avoid coining your own abbreviations; rephrase to avoid repetition of complex names. But if you *must* coin abbreviations, define them exactly at first use, and *never* use them in titles or abstracts.

List drugs, insecticides, and related preparations by their chemical names when possible, otherwise by generic names. For generic names consult the most recent editions of *The Pharmacopeia of the United States of America, The National Formulary, New and Nonofficial Drugs,* or lists of common names accepted by national scientific societies (e.g., names of insecticides approved by the Entomological Society of America). For substances not listed in these compendia, use a trade name, followed, the first time, by its chemical or scientific name in parentheses.

The chemical formulas of common and simple substances (H_2O, CO_2, HCl, NaCl) may be used in the text or in table headings, especially if such terms occur repeatedly, even though such formulas imply definite quantities. To write *5 ml of H_2O* is illogical, because the formula H_2O, strictly speaking, means 18 g (or parts by weight) of water. But here custom overrules logic.

Complex substances, especially organic compounds, should be given their full scientific names at least the first time they are used. Subsequently, the common names will serve. Use good judgment in selecting the common name; *phthalic acid* serves better than *1,2-benzenecarboxylic acid,* and *phenol* than *carbolic acid.* Avoid antiquated names such as *muriatic acid* for *hydrochloric acid, copperas* for *ferrous sulfate, blue vitriol* for *copper sulfate,* or *potash, soda, baryta, Glauber's salt, Rochelle salt,* etc.

References to quantities of inorganic salts or hydrated organic substances should specify the number of molecules of water of hydration in the quantity of the substance; thus, copper sulfate pentahydrate, sodium sulfate decahydrate, asparagine monohydrate, histidine monohydrochloride monohydrate, etc.

Many names of organic substances include numbers, letters, or syllables designating details of the chemical structure. Transcribe these accurately. There are several isomers of dinitrophenol, for instance, and the precise one used must be made clear. Check for errors in the use of the small capitals D and L in names of sugars and amino acids, and of a few other asymmetric substances. These prefixes signify the configurational family; they have nothing to do with the direction in which the substance rotates the plane of polarized light. L-Alanine is dextrorotatory; when you must indicate direction of rotation write L(+)-alanine. Prefix an italic *d* or *l* when the configurational relationship of the substance to D- or L-glyceraldehyde is unknown. These prefixes do denote the direction of rotation of the substance under a standard condition.

Indicate the italic *d* and *l* prefixes with a single underline, the small capital D and L prefixes with a double underline. Also indicate italics for the symbols of elements that occur in the names of many organic compounds (*O*-methyltyrosine, *S*-benzyl-*N*-phthaloylcysteine).

If you refer frequently to substances with complex and difficult names, draw the structures, labeling them with the proper name and a Roman numeral, and then refer in the text to *substance* (or *acid, ketone,* etc.) *III,* or *V* or *IX,* as you have labeled them.

Anatomical Nomenclature

The International Committee on Anatomical Nomenclature has prepared an official revised list of human gross anatomical terms in Latin (*Nomina Anatomica*, 2nd edition, 1961). Subcommittees are at work on standardization of terms in histology and embryology.

For species other than man, use terms based on the same principles: well-established terms should not be altered merely on pedantic or etymological grounds; each structure should be designated by one term only; differentiating adjectives should be arranged as opposites, e.g., major and minor.

For general purposes, the Latin form may be translated into the vernacular equivalent. In good English usage, some terms (e.g., femur, cisterna chyli) are not translated, others may or may not be (as: tela subcutanea or subcutaneous tissue), but most are given in anglicized form or English equivalent (e.g., brachial plexus *for* plexus brachialis, stomach *for* ventriculus). Avoid antiquated names and obsolete usage.

Nomenclature of Organisms

GENERAL PRINCIPLES

Biological nomenclature is designed to achieve stability and universal acceptance of scientific names of organisms. Authors and editors are obligated to accept the rules governing nomenclature in the *International Code of Botanical Nomenclature* (Lanjouw et al., 1956), the *International Code of Nomenclature of Bacteria and Viruses* (Buchanan et al., 1958), and the *International Code of Zoological Nomenclature* (Stoll et al., 1961).

Much useful and timely information on botanical nomenclature appears in *Taxon*; that on bacterial nomenclature appears in the *International Bulletin of Bacteriological Nomenclature and Taxonomy*. The essential features of zoological nomenclature also appear in *Procedure in Taxonomy* (Schenck and McMasters, 1956), and current developments are reported in *Systematic Zoology*. Lists of families, genera, and species are available from the Internationl Trust for Zoological Nomenclature, and official decisions on these names are published in *The Bulletin of Zoological Nomenclature*. Because of usage, and because of inherent differences among animals, plants, and microorganisms, the codes differ in certain basic principles and practices.

SYSTEMATIC
CATEGORIES

The basic taxa (*singular,* taxon), in descending order, are phylum or division, class, order, family, genus, and species. In all disciplines, the scientific name of a species is a binomial (botany), a binary combination (bacteriology), or a binomen (zoology) and consists of the generic name followed by the specific epithet (botany and bacteriology) or specific name (zoology). The scientific names of all taxa are Latin or latinized forms and are to be so treated.

To be validly published and to have standing in nomenclature, the name of a newly proposed taxon of Recent plants (not fossil plants), except bacteria, must be accompanied by a Latin description or a reference to a previously and effectively published Latin description. Effective dates of this requirement are 1 January 1935 for plants other than algae and 1 January 1958 for algae. Authors should not submit (or editors accept) manuscripts that violate this rule. The zoological and bacteriological codes do not require Latin diagnoses.

CAPITALIZATION

Do not use the specific name or epithet alone when referring to a species; it must be preceded by the generic name or its abbreviation. The generic name, however, or that of any higher rank, may stand by itself. Use initial capitals for names of genera and of all higher taxa. Generic names may be abbreviated to the capitalized initial letter when followed by a specific epithet (name), if the context makes the meaning clear. Never capitalize specific names (epithets) or subspecies taxa (except where permitted by the botanical code). Generic names used as vernacular names are neither italicized nor capitalized (*see* p. 70): *Petunia,* petunia; *Mastodon,* mastodon; *Bacillus,* bacillus; *Avena,* avena test.

INFRASPECIFIC
CATEGORIES

The three codes of nomenclature differ regarding subdivisions of species.

The botanical code recognizes taxa subordinate to species, such as subspecies, variety, subvariety, forma, and subforma (*Andropogon ternatus* subsp. *macrothrix; Saxifraga aizoon* var. *aizoon* subvar. *brevifolia* forma *multicaulis* subforma *surculosa).* The botanical term "variety" (abbreviated var. or v.) is restricted to variant forms of wild plants that have been given Latin names as true botanical varieties, even though they may have been brought into cultivation (*Viola tricolor* var. *hirta).*

The bacteriological code recognizes no infraspecific taxon subordinate to the rank of subspecies and considers variety synonymous with subspecies.

However, this code permits the use of such infraspecific taxa as strain, serotype, group, phase, forma specialis, variant, stage, and state.

The zoological code recognizes subspecies and will accept names for variety and forma up to 1961, but will not govern names in infrasubspecific categories.

HORTICULTURAL VARIETIES

Names of cultivated varieties of plants (cultivars) are printed in roman type set off with single quotes after the Latin names of the species (*Saintpaulia ionantha* 'Calico'; *Lycopersicum esculentum* 'Red Cherry'). Many cultivars have Latin names, which must be retained. Consult the *International Code of Nomenclature of Cultivated Plants* (Vilmorin et al., 1958).

CITATION OF AUTHOR

The person first publishing a scientific name for any taxon, under regulations prescribed by the codes, is its author. In taxonomic papers the name of a taxon should be supplemented with the name of its author (*Homo* Linnaeus; *Musca domestica* Linnaeus; *Magnolia grandiflora* Linnaeus; *Viràles* Breed, Murray and Hitchens, 1944; *Clostridium pasteurianum* Winogradsky). The author citation need appear only once in the article but usually not in the title.

When a species or subspecies is transferred to a genus other than that in which it was first placed, the name of the original author of the species is placed in parentheses. In botany and microbiology, the authority of the new combination follows, and is not placed in parentheses: *Shigella dysenteriae* (Shiga) Castellani and Chalmers, *Spiraea latifolia* (Ait.) Borkh. The zoological code does not recommend citing the authority of the new combination.

TYPOGRAPHY

Biological publications generally italicize scientific names of genera, subgenera, species, subspecies, and other subordinate taxa. New names of taxa above genera may be italicized, but this practice is not common. The names of taxa proposed as new to science, as new names or as new combinations, and appearing in print for the first time, are commonly set in boldface type. Generic names used as common names are neither italicized nor capitalized.

VERNACULAR OR COMMON NAMES

Many plants and animals are known by their vernacular (provincial, common) names, as well as their scientific names. Vernacular names for the same organism differ from language to language. Nomenclatural rules and customs in various disciplines concern themselves with the use of vernacular names.

The Entomological Society of America approves the common names of approximately 1,500 insects. The Society's rule is: "In the case of names having two parts, one of them a group name, a separate word will be used for the group name when used in a sense that is systematically correct. Example: 'house fly,' as contrasted with 'dobsonfly'." If an insect is truly a fly or bug use a two-word name (*house fly, bed bug*). If it is not a true fly or bug use a single word (*dobsonfly, sawfly, spittlebug*). Since no insect larva is a true worm, the suffix *worm* is always printed solid with the modifier: *silkworm* not *silk worm*. and *cutworm* not *cut worm*.

The American Ornithologists' Union (1957) publishes a check-list of North American birds with scientific names of species and subspecies, but vernacular names only for species. The names follow the *International Code of Zoological Nomenclature*.

Family names (e.g., Sciuridae, Chironomidae) may become vernacular names if the terminal *-ae* and the capital are dropped (sciurid, chironomid).

Common names of plants are seldom capitalized, although names derived from proper nouns may retain the initial capital letter, whether hyphenated or set as two words. Examples: Cupid's-dart, Dutchman's-pipe, English ivy, flower-of-Jove, Gray's lily. Proper names lose their capital letter in fanciful names: jack-in-the-pulpit, blue-eyed-mary, and brown-eyed-susan. Plant names ending in *bean, berry, bush, cup, flower, grass, lily, nut, pod, root, thorn,* and *wort* are usually printed solid.

An English common name may be coined from the scientific name of any bacterial genus. A generic name is a noun in the singular and requires a singular verb. Custom also sanctions the vernacular usage of plural generic names. Examples: The salmonella is . . . , but the salmonellae (brucellae, corynebacteria, clostridia, sarcinae) are . . . . The Latin plural of a generic name is preferred in bacteriology, but English plural endings are used exclusively for certain genera (pseudomonads for *Pseudomonas*) and sometimes for others (e.g., salmonellas, shigellas, vibrios, sarcinas). Occasionally more than one common name arises from a generic name, as treponema or treponeme from *Treponema,* and streptomycete or streptomyces from *Streptomyces.*

Keys for Identifying Organisms

The ideal key to a group of organisms presents rigorously selected information in such a way that a series of correct choices leads the user step by step to the identification of an organism. Identification results only if the key has been properly constructed, if the user interprets his material and the key correctly, and if the organism has been included in the key. Lawrence (1951) and Metcalf (1954) have presented helpful ideas on the construction of keys. Keys designed to show relationships or phylogeny tend to be less functional and to become only synopses of taxa. Keys provide primarily, except in the most specialized works, a useful and practical means of identifying organisms, but not necessarily an accurate picture of phylogenetic lines or natural relationships.

Several different types of keys appear in biological publications. Some keys separate only two species, others separate hundreds of taxa. The most useful keys have a dichotomous construction in the form of couplets permitting only one correct choice. Guiding principles for construction of a key are as follows (Metcalf, 1954):

1) Simplicity. Write entries in the keys as simple, direct, and mutually exclusive couplets; thus, a dichotomous key.
2) Clarity. State the first member of the couplet in the positive, and the second member as a negative or contrasting statement of the characters displayed in the first.
3) Reversibility. Construct the key so that it can be used backward as well as forward. Then if an erroneous choice is made at one couplet it is possible to retrace the steps and find the point of divergence.

Examples of keys that illustrate these principles are as follows:

Key to the families of the order *Myriangeales*
(after Wolf and Wolf, 1947)

A. Asci arising at different levels
    B. Stroma massive, of homogeneous texture,
        without a rind . . . . Family 1: *Myriangiaceae*
    BB. Stroma effuse, interior gelatinous,
        exterior crustose . . . . Family 2: *Elsinoeaceae*
AA. Asci arising at one level
    C. Stroma naked . . . . Family 3: *Saccardiaceae*
    CC. Stroma with crustose rind
        D. Multiloculate . . . . Family 4: *Dothioraceae*
        DD. Uniloculate or perithecium-
           like . . . . Family 5: *Pseudosphaeriaceae*

Key to the genera of the family *Heteromyidae*
(after Cockrum, 1957)

1.   Soles of hind feet densely haired; interparietal less than one-fourth of greatest width of skull   2

1′.   Soles of hind feet naked, or haired only from heel to plantar surface; interparietal more than one-fourth of greatest width of skull   3

2(1).   Length of hind foot more than 32 mm; tip of tail tufted; occlusal surface of upper premolars elliptical . . . . *Dipodomys*

2′.   Length of hind foot less than 32 mm; tip of tail not tufted; occlusal surface of upper premolars rectangular . . . . *Microdipodops*

3(1′). Pelage silky or hispid, never spiny; upper incisors grooved; bullae excessively inflated . . . . *Perognathus*

3′.   Pelage spiny; upper incisors ungrooved; bullae slightly inflated (not reaching level of grinding surfaces of molars) . . . . *Liomys*

Quotation   Quotations are often necessary for documentation. They should be limited to essential passages. Selected phrases are superior to long quotations requiring additional explanation. Unless the quotation is brief and pointed, a paraphrase or résumé is preferable.

Quotations should reproduce the original *exactly* in spelling, capitalization, italics, and punctuation. If irregularities are quoted, they should be immediately followed by [sic] to assure the reader that you have quoted accurately. If you italicize part of a quotation, say so in parentheses: "omit *useless* words" (my italics). Note that the parentheses are outside the quotation marks but inside the period.

Enclose in square brackets any words you insert within a quotation: "by van Slyke's [manometric] method." Do not use parentheses. Parentheses around your own remarks within another's statement falsely identify your remarks as his. Add brackets by hand if your typewriter lacks them. Indicate an ellipsis within a quoted sentence by three *spaced* periods (*see* Period, p. 18).

Type all quotations double-spaced (for use of quotation marks, *see* p. 22–23) .

Quotations of 10 or more printed lines from copyrighted works normally require permission from author or publisher. But the rules of publishing houses vary. Some publishers require permission only for quotations of more than 250 or 300 words. In 1962 members of The Association of American University Presses (which does not include commercial publishers) passed the following "Resolution on Permission" to quote:

1) That publications issued under our imprints may be quoted without specific prior permission in works of original scholarship for accurate citation of authority or for criticism, review, or evaluation, subject to the conditions listed below.
2) That appropriate credit be given in the case of each quotation.
3) That waiver of the requirement for specific permission does not extend to quotations that are complete units in themselves (as poems, letters, short stories, essays, journal articles, complete chapters or sections of books, maps, charts, graphs, tables, drawings, or other illustrative materials), in whatever form they may be reproduced; nor does the waiver extend to quotation of whatever length presented as primary material for its own sake (as in anthologies or books of readings).
4) The fact that specific permission for quoting of material may be waived under this agreement does not relieve the quoting author and publisher from the responsibility of determining "fair use" of such material.

When asking permission to quote, identify the material by full, accurate references. The initial copyright period is 28 years in the United States; one 28-year renewal is permitted.

Footnotes   Use footnotes *only when clearly necessary* for presenting explanatory material that does not justify a place in the text or tables. Examples of recommended footnotes are change of author's address, prescribed statements relating to dissertation, institutional approval, and contribution number, if necessary. Indicate a footnote in the text by a superior number ([1, 2, 3]). Place reference numbers after the word or statement annotated. Number footnotes consecutively throughout the manuscript, starting with those on the title page. Type footnotes for the text double-spaced on a separate page with each entry as a separate paragraph headed by the number corresponding to its citation in the text.

Footnotes to tables should be placed at the foot of the table and not on a separate page. To identify each footnote, use either a symbol or a superscript letter (*see* p. 57 and footnotes to Tables 5 and 6).

Never use a footnote or a literature citation in an abstract. Avoid use of footnotes to titles.

Acknowledgments

A section headed ACKNOWLEDGMENTS may be placed between the text and LITERATURE CITED. Avoid acknowledgments as footnotes to the title or to words in the text. Do not use a credit line (with the technical assistance of . . .) immediately after the name of the author(s) because the person credited may be inadvertently cited as an author.

In this section you may acknowledge grants-in-aid, and statements, tables, or figures borrowed from published material. It is courteous to ask the author and editor for permission to reproduce even material that is not copyrighted. Copyright owners sometimes specify the phrasing for credit lines.

Literature Cited

Basic considerations in making bibliographic references are accuracy, readers' convenience, and librarians' time.

In the text, citations should be made consistent (according to the practice of the journal) by use of one of the following systems:

1) *Name-and-year system.* Depending upon the construction of the sentence, the citation will appear as Smith and Jones (1960), or (Smith and Jones, 1960). When there are three authors, name all in the first citation, e.g., Doe, Miller, and Wilson (1960), but subsequently use Doe et al. (1960). When there are four or more authors cite their paper in the form Doe et al. (1960).

2) *Number system.* Depending upon the construction of the sentence, the citation will appear as Smith and Jones (1), or (Smith and Jones, 1) or simply (1). If citations are to be numbered, number them after all additions and deletions have been made.

List literature citations or references at the end of your paper in alphabetical order by authors. Include only those references cited in the text. Do not cite unpublished work unless the paper has been accepted for publication. Unpublished results may be mentioned as such in the text with the word (*unpublished*) in parentheses after the author's name. References should contain all the data necessary to locate the source easily in a library. Check all parts of each reference against the original. An inaccurate or incomplete reference wastes time of readers and librarians and reflects on the scholarship of the author.

Most journals have their own style for capitals, italics, boldface, and so on, in literature citations. Be sure to consult a recent issue. Literature citations must be typewritten and double-spaced.

The critical items for literature citations follow:

1) *Authorship.* The family name of the first or sole author precedes the initials or given name. Cite names of all co-authors as given in the by-line.

It is usually not difficult to invert the family and given names of the first or sole author in preparing a reference list. Personal names in many countries usually correspond in form to *John C. Smith,* and can be easily inverted *(Smith, John C.).* But designations of rank within a family and compound and hyphenated family names of foreign origin may present problems.

Junior (Jr.) and designations of rank within a family, such as *II* and *III,* are indicated after the initials (F. W. Day, Jr., inverts to Day, F. W., Jr.; C. G. Child II to Child, C. G. II.). The Spanish word *hijo* (h.) means *son* and is equivalent to *junior,* and should be so translated: Gonzalo Ley (hijo) becomes Ley, G., Jr. Also maintain the maternal name in Spanish; *Casimir Gómez Ortega* inverts to *Gómez-Ortega, C.* not *Ortega, C. G.,* and *Juan Pérez y Fernández* inverts to *Pérez y Fernández, J.*

Compound and hyphenated *American* family names, irrespective of origin, are treated in the same manner as other American names:

Examples	*Invert to*
Henri Vander-Brink	Vander-Brink, Henri
C. B. van Niel	Van Niel, C. B.
R. P. De Smet	De Smet, R. P.
S. Bayne-Jones	Bayne-Jones, S.
J. de Bueno	De Bueno, J.
T. l'Eltore	L'Eltore, T.

Compound family names in publications from other countries (Canada, Czechoslovakia, England, Finland, Germany, Italy, Poland, Scandinavia, Spain, USSR, etc.) are similarly inverted and the particles are capitalized.

For *Brazilian* and *Portuguese* names the particles *(do, da, dos, das)* follow the initials or given name:

Silvio do Amaral	Amaral, Silvio do
A. C. dos Santos	Santos, A. C. dos

In *Chinese* publications the family name precedes the given name (usually hyphenated):

Chen Tai-chien	Chen, Tai-Chien
Lin Ke-sheng	Lin, Ke-Sheng

But in American and British journals *Chinese* names are usually anglicized and inverted:

C. Ying Chang	Chang, C. Ying
Hsi Fan Fu	Fu, Hsi Fan

With *Dutch* names, particles and particle phrases follow initials when inverted:

L. A. de Vries	Vries, L. A. de
Willem van Eyck	Eyck, Willem van
J. van der Hoeve	Hoeve, J. van der
L. W. van Horts van Bing	Horts van Bing, L. W. van

Egyptian and other *Arabic* proper family names appear last:

Hassan Fahmy Khalil	Khalil, Hassan Fahmy
Mohamed Metwali Naguib	Naguib, Mohamed Metwali

When either prefixes and their variants (*el, ibn, abdel, abd-el, abdoul, abu, abou, aboul*) or the particle *el* alone precedes a name, either should be hyphenated to the name it precedes:

Aly Abdel Aziz	Abdel-Aziz, Aly
Youssef Abou-el-Ezz	Abou-el-Ezz, Youssef
Aziz Ibn Saud	Ibn-Saud, Aziz
Kamel el Metwali	el-Metwali, Kamel
Hedieh Khalil el Agouz	el-Agouz, Hedieh Khalil

In compound *French* names, the definite article (*le, la, les*) or combination with the preposition *de* (*du, de la, des*) precedes the family name. *De* (or *d'*) alone follows the initials:

J. Le Beau	Le Beau, J.
R. L'Epée	L'Epée, R.
V. du Bary	Du Bary, V.
A. de Bary	Bary, A. de
B. d'Aubiac	Aubiac, B. d'

The particles (*im, von, zu, zum, zur*) and their abbreviations in *German* names follow initials when inverted, and should be spelled out:

C. von Holt	Holt, C. von
H. zur Horst-Meyer	Horst-Meyer, H. zur
Ludwig v. Obersteg	Obersteg, Ludwig von

In *Hungarian* the family name regularly precedes the given name and inversion is unnecessary.

Farkas Karoly	Farkas, Karoly
Szent-Györgyi Albert	Szent-Györgyi, Albert

If *Sen* or *Das* precedes an *Indian* name, include it with the family name:

B. C. Sen Gupta	Sen Gupta, B. C.
K. P. Das Gupta	Das Gupta, K. P.

All elements of *Vietnamese* or *Thai* names are taken in the order in which they appear in the journal, joined by hyphens, and lower case is used for the second element:

Nguyen Lam Tiep	Nguyen-lam-Tiep

2) The *year* of publication follows the authorship:
Jones, T. C., and R. Doe. 1959.

When more than one paper or book by the same author(s) has appeared in a given year, the letters *a, b,* etc., should be used after the year (e.g., Smith, 1959*a, b*). In the references each entry should be typed separately, with the same letters after the date as appeared in the text (e.g., Smith, R. P. 1959*a*, Smith, R. P. 1959*b*).

For the name of one author or of identical authors listed in the same order, the editor may substitute a 3-em dash (————) in repeated entries.

3) The *title* must appear exactly as it does on the first page of the article or on the title page of the book.

4) *Abbreviations* are commonly used for the names of serial publications, except for one-word names. Follow the abbreviations listed by The American Standards Association (*see* examples, p. 82). If no abbreviation is found, use the rules of the American Standards Association, which are summarized as follows:

a) Never abbreviate the title of a journal consisting of a single word. Example: Phytopathology

b) Do not abbreviate the title of a journal consisting of several words so much that the journal cannot be recognized.

c) Never abbreviate personal names when they begin a journal name. Example: Hoppe-Seyler's Z. Physiol. Chem.

d) Form the abbreviation by omitting a continuous group of the final letters of the word; terminate it, if possible, after a consonant. Example: Biol., not bio. for biology.

e) The order of abbreviations in a title should be the same as the word order in the complete title. But in a long title some of the final words may be omitted. Never include abbreviations of subtitles.

f) Omit articles, conjunctions, and prepositions.

g) Capitalize the initial letter of the first element of the abbreviation. For the remainder, capitalize the first letter of each element, all letters, or none. Examples:

> Amer. J. Physiol.
> AMER. J. PHYSIOL.
> Amer. j. physiol.

h) For compound words, abbreviate only the final element. Example: Bodenforsch. *for* Bodenforschung.

i) Use either a period or a space between abbreviations of title words. If a space is used, each element must begin with a capital letter.

j) Diacritical marks may be used in an abbreviation but are not required. Be consistent.

5) *Volume and pages of serials* appear in arabic numbers after the abbreviated name of the periodical: 2: 120–136. An issue, number, supplement, or other part within a volume is shown in parentheses only when paged independently: 2(4): 1–56; 34 (Suppl. 2): 1–26. Any special series (Ser. 3, III, or C) precedes the volume number: Ser. 3, 2: 120–136; III, 2(4): 1–56; C, 2: 120–136.

6) In *book citations* the year of publication and title follow the authorship. The following appear in sequence after the title: the edition if other than the first, the publisher's name or shortened name (according to the *Cumulative Book Index*), the place of publication, and the number of pages if one volume, but the number of volumes if more. If particular pages are cited mention them in the text.

7) *Illustrations* are not mentioned unless they are separately paged from the text or are of particular importance.

8) For *transliteration* of words from Greek and Russian, *see* p. 42 and 43

9) *Missing bibliographic details* added for clarity (names, dates, publishers, etc.) should appear in brackets. For exceptions consult Bryant (1951).

10) Unpublished *documents* and other *source material* should be cited within parentheses in the text rather than in the **Literature Cited**. For example: (R. W. Smith, *personal communication*) (J. K. Jones, *unpublished data*).

EXAMPLES   Various types or categories of problems encountered in citing references are listed below in boldface type, and examples are given.

Author: Name as in by-line; Abstract:

Hildebrandt, Albert C. 1948. Influence of some carbon compounds on growth of plant tissue cultures in vitro. Anat. Rec. 100:674. (Abstr.)

Author: Prefix in name anglicized; Miscellaneous publication:

Van Dersal, W. R. 1938. Native woody plants of the United States, their erosion-control and wildlife values. U.S. Dep. Agr. Misc. Publ. 303. 362 p.

Author: Prefix in French name not anglicized; Pages separated:

Bary, A. de. 1886. Ueber einige Sclerotinien und Sclerotienkrankheiten. Bot. Zeit. 44:377–387, 393, 404, 409–426, 433–441, 449–461, 465–474.

Author: Hyphenated name (Compound name, without hyphen); Subtitle:

Gwynne-Vaughan, Helen. 1922. Fungi; Ascomycetes, Ustilaginales, Uredinales. Cambridge Univ. Press, London. 232 p.

Author: Transliterated names; Volume omitted; Each issue numbered independently:

Gavrilov, K. A., and T. S. Perel. 1958. Earthworms and other invertebrates in the soil under forests in Vologda region [in Russian]. Pochvovedenie 1958(8):133–140.

Author: Transliterated name; English title on original; Annals of Society; Number paged separately; Summary in English:

Nishikado, Y. 1921. On a disease of the grape cluster caused by *Physalospora baccae* Cavara [in Japanese, English summary]. Phytopathol. Soc. Japan, Annu. 1(4):20–42.

Author: Committee chairman; Preposition omitted from name of publication:

Riker, A. J. [*Chairman*]. 1952. Literature citations; how biologists like them. AIBS (Amer. Inst. Biol. Sci.) Bull. 2(1):18–19.

Author: Society committee; One-word serial name not abbreviated.

American Phytopathological Society, Committee on Standardization of Fungicidal Tests. 1943. Definitions of fungicide terms. Phytopathology 33:624–626.

Author: Service agency, omitted as publisher:

Chemical Abstracts Service. 1961. Chemical Abstracts list of periodicals with key to library files. American Chemical Society. Washington, D.C. 397 p.

Author: State institution; Fiscal year; Special part; Bulletin:

Wisconsin Agricultural Experiment Station. 1950. What's new in farm science; 66th annual report 1948/49. Part I. Wisconsin Agr. Exp. Sta. Bull. 491. 88 p.

Author: Federal agency; Two or more volumes:

U. S. Bureau of the Census. 1927. United States census of agriculture. 1925. U. S. Government Printing Office, Washington. 3 vol.

Author: Federal agency; Pages not numbered:

U. S. Department of Agriculture. Plant Pest Control Division, Pesticide Regulation Section. 1957. A summary of certain pesticide chemical uses. Loose leaf. n. p.

Author: Federal agency (omitted as publisher); Revised edition:

U. S. Government Printing Office. 1959. Style manual. Revised ed. Washington, D.C. 492 p.

Book:

Schwarts, R. J. 1955. The complete dictionary of abbreviations. T. Y. Crowell Co., New York. 211 p.

Book, Part of:

Overstreet, H. A. 1925. The psychology of effective writing, p. 87–109. *In* H. A. Overstreet, Influencing human behavior. Norton, New York.

Bulletin:

Bryant, Margaret S. 1951. Bibliographic style. U. S. Dep. Agr. Bibliogr. Bull. 16. 30 p.

Documents not published in conventional manner:

Annual report:

McClellan, R. O., J. R. McKenney, and L. K. Bustad. 1961. Metabolism and dosimetry of cesium-137 in rems, p. 55–59. *In* Hanford biology research annual report for 1960. HW-69500 (Hanford Laboratories, Richland, Wash.)

Nuclear Science Series reference; distributor cited:

Finston, H. L., and M. T. Kinsley, 1961. The radiochemistry of cesium. Nat. Acad. Sci., Nuclear Sci. Ser. NAS-NS-3035. Office of Technical Services, Dep. of Commerce, Washington, D.C.

Progress report:

Auerbach, S. I., and R. M. Anderson. 1959. Ecological research, p. 18-54. *In* Physics Division annual progress report for period ending 31 July 1959. ORNL-2806 (Oak Ridge National Laboratory. Tenn.)

Technical Report; double reference:

Gloyna, E. F., E. R. Hermann, and W. R. Dryman. 1955. Oxidation ponds—waste treatment studies, radioisotope uptake, and algae concentration. Univ. Texas, Dep. Civil Eng. Tech. Rep. No. 2. (*Also* AECU-3113).

Translation:

Nakaya, T. 1960. Biological, geological and chemical studies on Sr^{90}, Cs^{137} in fresh water regions. [Transl. from Japanese] p. 5 to 8. USAEC-tr-4245.

Illustrations not included in pagination, and important:

Smith, E. F. 1917. Mechanism of tumor growth in crowngall. J. Agr. Res. 8:165–183; Fig. 4-65.

Newspaper (pages separated):

Maverick, M. 1944. The case against "gobbledygook." New York Times Magazine. 21 May: 11, 35–36.

Paper in a collection or book by various authors:

Link, G. K. K. 1928. Bacteria in relation to plant diseases, p. 590 to 606. *In* E. O. Jordan and I. S. Falk [ed.] The newer knowledge of bacteriology and immunology. Univ. Chicago Press, Chicago.

Patent: original not seen:

Penn, F. H. 1942. Hydrogenated butter method. U. S. Pat. 2,272,578 Feb. 10 Abstr. in Offic. Gaz. U. S. Patent Office 535:322.

Proceedings of Society; Series:

Salaman, R. N., and F. C. Bawden. 1932. Analysis of some necrotic virus diseases of the potato. Roy. Soc. (London), Proc., B. 111:53–73.

Thesis on microfilm:

Rafferty, Nancy S. 1958. A study of the relationship between the pronephros and the haploid syndrome in frog larvae. Ph.D. Thesis. Univ. Illinois (Libr. Congr. Card No. Mic. 58-5479) 41 p. Univ. Microfilms. Ann Arbor, Mich. (Diss. Abstr. 19:1146) .

Transactions of society:

Vose, G. P. 1963. Thermal destruction of bone as seen with the electron microscope. Amer. Microscop. Soc., Trans. 82:48–54.

Two papers in same year, lettered when citations not numbered; Name repeated:

Magoon, M. L., R. W. Hougas, and D. C. Cooper. 1958*a*. Cytogenetic studies of tetraploid hybrids in *Solanum* from hexaploid-diploid matings. J. Hered. 49:171–178.

Magoon, M. L., R. W. Hougas, and D. C. Cooper. 1958*b*. Cytogenetic studies of complex hybrids in *Solanum*. J. Hered. 49:285–293.

In the typewritten copy of the literature citations repeat all names of multiple authors. Editors or printers may later insert a 3-em dash (————) for the names in consecutive citations after the first.

ABBREVIATIONS OF WORDS USED IN CITATIONS

Titles of journals can be abbreviated by combining the abbreviations of the words or word stems listed below (single word titles are not abbreviated). The abbreviation appears in boldface type. The list is adapted from one prepared by The American Standards Association, Sectional Committee Z39 on Library Work and Documentation.

Abhandlung-
Abstract
Abteilung
Academ-
Accadem-
Administr-
Advance-
Aerologicheskii
Aeromedica,
  Aeromedic-
Aeronaut-
Aerzteblatt
Africa
Agraire, **Agr**alia,
  Agrar-, **Agrarnyi**,
  Agricol-, **Agricult**-,
  Agrikult-
Agrobotanica

Agrogeological
Agronom-
Akadem-
Algologi-
Allgemein
Amendment
America-, **Amerika**-
Anaesthes-,
  Anaesthetist
Anais, **Anal**e
Anal-
Anatom-
Angewandt-
Animal-
Annaes, **Annal**
Anniversary
Annotation-
Announcement

Annual, **Annuale**,
  Annuario
Anorganisch
Anthropolog-
Antibiotic
Antimicrobial
Anual-, **Anuar**-
Apicole
Apicolt-
Apicult-
Apothecary,
  Apotheker
Appendix
Applicada, **Applicat**-,
  Applied, **Applique**
Arbeit-, **Arbete**-
Arboriculture
Archaeolog-

Archeolog-
Archiv-, Archiwum
Arhiv
Arkhiv
Arquiv
Asociacion
Associa-
Astronom-
Astrophys-
Atmosfaer-,
    Atmosfar-,
    Atmosfer-,
    Atmosphar-,
    Atmospher-
Atomic
Auditory
Automatic
Avance-
Avhandling-

Bacolog-
Bacteriolog-
Bakteriolog-
Batteriolog-
Behavior
Beiheft
Beilage
Beitrag
Belg-
Bericht
Bibliograf-,
    Bibliograph-
Bibliotec-,
    Bibliotek-,
    Bibliothec-,
    Bibliothek,
    Bibliotheque
Biennial

Biochem-
Biochim-
Biodynamica
Biofizika
Biogeochimique
Biogeograph-
Biograf-, Biograph-
Biokhim-
Bioklimatologie
Biolog-, Bioloskih
Biomedical
Biophysic-
Bioquimica
Biotheoretic-
Biuletyn, Biulleten
Bjuletin
Bodenforschung
Bodenkunde
Bohemosloven-
Boletim
Bolgarskii
Bollettino
Botan-
Bratislav-
Britain, Britanni-,
    British
Bryology-
Buleten
Bulgarian
Bulletin-, Bullettino
Bureau

Canad-
Cardiolog-
Cartografica,
    Cartographie
Catalog-
Cechoslov-

Centennial
Centraal, Central-
Ceskoslovensk-
Chemi-
Chinese
Chirurg-
Chromatography
Chroni-
Ciencia-
Cientifica
Circular
Cirkulaer
Cirugia
Class-
Climatolog-
Clini-
Colegio
Collaboration,
    Collaborazione
College
Comerci-, Commerce
Commission,
    Committee
Communic-
Company
Compar-
Compte, Comptes
Comunic-
Confederation
Conference
Congres-
Conserv-
Contribut-
Cooperat-
Corporation
Cryptogam-
Cultur-, Cultuur
Cytochem-

Cytolog-
Czechoslovak

Decennial
Demographie
Dendrolog-
Dent-
Departament-,
   Departement-,
   Department-
Dermatolog-
Deutsch-
Digest-
Direc-, Direcc-,
   Direct-, Direkt-
Disease
Disserta-
Divis-
Document-
Doklad-
Dokument

Ecolog-
Econom-
Edition, Editor
Educa-
Egyet-
Egyptian
Ekolog-
Electrochem-
Electrochim-
Electrolog-
Electrotechnical
Embriolog-
Embryol-
Encyclopedia
Endocrinolog-
Engineer-

Enolog-
Entomolog-
Enzymolog-
Epidemiolog-
Escola-
Espan-
Essential
Ethnograf-,
   Ethnograph-
Ethnolog-
Etudes
Eugenics
Europe-
Evolution
Examination
Exchange
Exhibit-
Experiment-
Extension
Extract

Facolt-, Faculd-,
   Facult-
Fakult-
Farmaceut-,
   Farmacevt-,
   Farmaci-,
   Farmaco
Farmacolog-
Federac-, Federal-
Finland-
Finn-
Fitolog-
Floricoltura
Floristica
Flugblatt
Forest-
Forsch-

Foundation
Fysiograf-
Fysiolog-

Gazet-, Gazett-
Gemolog-
Genel, General-
Genet-
Genitourinary
Geochem-
Geochim-
Geodaes-, Geodaet-,
   Geodas-, Geodat-,
   Geodes-, Geodet-,
   Geodez-
Geograf-, Geograph-
Geolog-
Geomagnetism
Geophys-
Geriatri-
German-
Gerontolog-
Gesellschaft
Gesundheit
Gibridizatsiia
Gidrobiol-
Gidrolog-
Gigiena
Giornale
Glaciology
Graduate
Gynecolog-

Haematolog-
Helveti-
Hematolog-
Herbari-
Heredit-

Histochem-
Histolog-
Histor-
Horticol-, **Hort**icult-,
   Hortikult-,
   Hortique
Hospit-
Hungar-
Husbandry
Hydrograf-
Hydrolog-
Hygien-

Ichthyolog-
Illustr-
Immigration
Immunitatsforschung
Immunolog-
Imperial-
Importacao,
   Importacion,
   Importation,
   Importazione
Imunolog-
Incorporated
Industr-
Infect-
Infekt-
Inorganic
Institucao,
   Institucio-,
   Institut-,
   Instytut
Interamerica
Internal
International
Investiga-
Iranicus

Itali-

Jaarboek
Jahresbericht
Japan-, **Jap**on-
Jardim, **Jard**in-
Jewish
Jornal, **J**ournal
Jugoslav-

Katalog
Kem-
Klass-
Klini-
Kommission,
   Kommitte
Kommun-
Konfer-
Kongres, **Kong**ress

Laboratoire,
   Laborator-
Landwirtschaft-
Language
Latin, **Lat**inus
Latinoamericana
Leaflet
Lebanese
Lebensmittel
Lectur-
Leningrad-
Librair-, **Libra**ry
Lichenolog-
Limnolog-
Linguistic
Literar-, **Literatur-**
Lithuanian

Magazin
Malacolog-
Malariolog-
Mammalog-
Management
Mathemat-
Mechanic-
Medecin-, **Med**ic-,
   Meditsin-,
   Medizin-,
   Medycyna,
   Medyczny
Memento, **Mem**oir-,
   Memorand-,
   Memoryal,
   Memuary
Mental-
Method-
Metrolog-
Mexic-
Micologia
Microbiolog-
Microscop-
Mikologi-
Mineral-,
   Mineralog-
Minerolog-
Minister-, **Minist**r-
Miscelan-, **Miscellan-**
Modern-
Molecul-
Monograf-,
   Monograph
Morpholog-
Moskovskii
Municip-
Muse-
Mycolog-

Nation-, Natirali,
  Natirelles
Natur-
Naturforschung
Nederland-
Netherlands
Neurobiolog-
Neurolog-
Neurosurgery
New England
New Series
New Zealand
Nippon-
Nord-
Nuclear-

Observ-
Occupation-,
  Occupazione
Oceanograf-,
  Oceanograph-
Ocular-
Offici-
Ophthalmolog-
Optic-, Opticheskii,
  Optik-, Optique,
  Optisch
Optometry
Organic-,
  Organicheskii,
  Organique
Organisat-,
  Organizac-,
  Organizat-,
  Organize-,
  Organizing,
  Organizzazione
Orient-

Original-, Origineel
Otolaryngolog-
Otolog-

Paleontolog-
Pamflet,
  Pamietnik-,
  Pamphlet-
Parasitenkunde
Parasitolog-
Patent
Pathogen
Patholog-
Pediatr-
Pharmaceut-,
  Pharmaci-,
  Pharmacy,
  Pharmazeut-,
  Pharmazie
Philosoph-,
  Philoszophia
Photograaf,
  Photograf-
Physica-,
  Physicist, Physics,
  Physicu-, Physik-,
  Physique-
Physiolog-
Phytolog-
Phytopatholog-
Polish, Polnisch,
  Polon-, Polski
Pomolog-
Populae, Populair,
  Popular-
Postgraduate
Prehistori-
Prelimin-

Proceeding
Professional,
  Profession-
Project-, Projekt
Psychiatr-
Psycholog-
Psychopharmacology
Publication
Publisher

Quantitativ-
Quarterly

Radiation
Radioactive
Radiobiolog-
Radiolog-
Reclamation
Record, Recueil
Registr-
Religious
Rendu, Rendus
Report
Reproduction
Repubblica, Republ-
Research
Review, Revista,
  Revue
Rhumatologie
Rivista
Romanian
Royal
Rumanian
Russ-

Scandinavi-
Schrift-
Schweizer-

Scien-
Scotland, Scottish
Sectio-
Seismolog-
Serie, Series
Serolog-
Silvicult-
Simposio
Social-, Sociedad-,
   Societ-
Sovet-
Special-
Station, Stazione
Statist-
Street
Stud-
Sumar-, Summar-
Supplement-
Surg-
Survey
Swed-
Switzerland
Sympos-
System-

Taxonom-
Techni-
Technolog-
Tijdschrift
Topograf-,
   Topograph
Toxicolog-
Transaction,
   Transazione
Translation
Travail, Travaux
Treasurer, Treasury
Tropic-, Tropik-,
   Tropique,
   Tropisch
Trud-
Turkish, Turkiye
Typograf-,
   Typograph

Ukrain-
Union of Soviet
   Socialist Republics
United Kingdom
United Nations

United States
United States of
   America
Universidad-,
   Universit-,
   Universytet
Urolog-

Virolog-
Virusforschung
Vitaminolog-
Viticult-
Volume

Weekblad
Wetenschapp-
Wissenschaft
Wochenschrift

Zeitschrift
Zeitung
Zentralblatt
Zhirovoi
Zhurnal
Zoolog-

3. Approval of Manuscripts and Release of Results

Some institutions require the author to obtain approval from a responsible official within his institution before submitting a manuscript. Whether required or not, official approval safeguards staff members against erroneous or premature publication and gives opportunity for editorial improvement and review.

Technical information should not be released to the press without permission of both the investigator and the responsible administrator.

The first report of technical or scientific information should be published in a scientific journal or presented before a scientific society. Release to news services may coincide. The investigator should, whenever possible, check the press report carefully before its release.

The intent of these statements is not to advocate censorship, but to protect all concerned, including the press, against embarrassing errors.

4. Review of Manuscripts

Editors customarily send each manuscript to qualified reviewers who can help the author avoid error or misunderstanding, and who may strengthen and clarify his presentation. Reviewers may identify themselves, but usually they remain anonymous. Whether their criticisms are appreciated or not, reviewers are on the author's side. An author should take the reviewer's comments seriously and answer criticisms by improving his manuscript, not by debate. Misunderstanding by the reviewer usually arises from lack of clarity in the manuscript. Few papers are accepted outright. If the author rejects an important suggestion, he should tell the editor why. The editor is responsible only for the form of the published paper, and the author remains responsible for all statements in it.

Note to Reviewers If a manuscript is too long the author will not be helped by the comment, "This manuscript is too long. Condense it to half." Give specific directions for eliminating unimportant portions or condensing expanded writing. Indicate grammatical and rhetorical errors (keep your own remarks free from similar errors). Avoid changing the author's style if his meaning is clear and if the text is neither verbose nor cryptic. Be considerate. One test of a good critique is whether you would be willing to sign it. Keep an open mind. Do not consider your opinions infallible. Although there is real danger of rejecting a "breakthrough" manuscript as "crackpot," the major problem is the publication of papers that lack sufficient data and controls. Treat the manuscript as confidential.

Consider the following:

1) Return two copies of the criticism, one of which the editor may send to the author. Copies may or may not be signed.
2) Avoid acrimony.
3) Grade the paper as superior, good, acceptable (with revision), or unacceptable on both its scientific merit and its form. Also advise the editor on the suitability and acceptability of the abstract.
4) Return manuscripts and comments promptly. Advise the editor if you anticipate a delay of more than 2 weeks.
5) Ask yourself the following questions:
   a) Has the material been published previously in the same or similar form?
   b) Do all parts warrant publication? The American Documentation Institute, Auxiliary Publication Service (administered by the Library of Congress), accepts for permanent deposit supplementary material (tabular data, illustrations, flow sheets, reference lists) for papers in journals. By arrangement, an editor may place a note (giving accession number and price) in a paper, stating that auxiliary material is on deposit and available to anyone as a photocopy.
   c) Is the manuscript more suitable for some other journal?
   d) Is the manuscript in proper form? You may suggest minor corrections in diction, style, etc., on the manuscript. Use light pencil, *not ink.*
   e) Is the arrangement of the paper satisfactory and economical? Have any ideas been under- or over-emphasized? Should parts be expanded, condensed, or omitted? Is there unnecessary repetition or duplication? Make specific suggestions.
   f) Is the author's writing clear? If not, suggest improvements. If he has any bad writing habits, indicate tactfully how he may correct them.
   g) Can you suggest improvements for the illustrations? Are any of the illustrations unnecessary? Are more needed? Are they numbered and

lettered? Will the smallest lettering be clear after the necessary reduction?

h) Are there errors of fact, interpretation, or calculation?

i) Are the technical and experimental methods adequate?

j) Do the tables present the data clearly and concisely?

k) Does the author have adequate knowledge of the pertinent literature? Are too many or too few citations listed? Are citations in the proper form?

5. Copy Editing

Before type can be set, instructions to the printer must be placed on the manuscript. This is the function of the copy editor. You can assist him by carefully adhering to the following instructions, by accurately indicating italics, capitalization, and the order and relative importance of the headings. Items that must be considered are the following.

Type Face
ITALICS
(marked by single underlining)

Use italics for

1) names of books and periodicals in the text, but not in the literature cited

2) most foreign words and phrases and their abbreviations, but not for proper names. Many foreign words are now widely used in English and need not be set in italics (a priori, attache, in vitro, in vivo, et al.)

3) mathematical matter for all unknowns and constants (but use roman for differential d in dy/dx, for abbreviations of trigonometric functions, and log)

4) scientific names of genera, species, subspecies, and varieties; names of higher taxa may be italicized

5) letters or numbers in text which refer to corresponding letters or numbers in an illustration
6) single letters or words under discussion in the text
7) letters used as symbols for genes and alleles (but not for chromosomes and blood groups)
8) first occurrence of a special term
9) emphasis on words or phrases only when other means of emphasis are not satisfactory (overuse destroys the emphasis)
10) titles and legends for tables and figures (*see* p. 50 and 55)
11) cross-reference and index expressions: *see* and *see also*

SMALL CAPITALS
(marked by double underlining)

Follow the style of the journal to which the paper is to be submitted. Some journals use small capitals for AD (AD 65), BC (in 31 BC), PM, AM, and for abbreviations of government or international agencies such as AEC, UNESCO. See page 65 for the use of small capitals in names of chemical compounds. Use small capitals for

1) headings for figures and tables: FIG. 1; TABLE 2. In the text abbreviate *figure* (Fig.) but not *table* (Table)
2) SD (standard deviation)
3) SE (standard error)
4) N (normality)
5) M (molarity)
6) LD$_{50}$ (lethal dose, median), ID$_{50}$ (infective dose, median), etc., but MLD (minimal lethal dose)
7) D and L as configurational prefixes

CAPITALS
(marked by triple underlining only where intention is not clear)

Use initial capitals for

1) proper nouns and some proper adjectives. But words that have been derived from proper nouns and that have a specialized meaning need not be capitalized: *petri dish, paris green, bunsen burner, italicize, pasteurize.*
2) first word of each sentence
3) first word and proper names in titles of books and journal articles in literature citations
4) the terms of official titles of courtesy when the titles must be used
5) the official names of private or government organizations and institutions, but not the shortened forms of such names unless necessary to avoid ambiguity

6) generic geographical terms that follow a proper name (river; Mississippi River, but Snake and Columbia rivers)

7) names of historical epochs, geologic ages and strata, zoogeographic zones, and other terms used for convenience of classification (The terms *age, era, epoch, period, till, glaciation,* and others need not be capitalized unless ambiguity might result: Neolithic age; Stone Age; Ice Age; Pleistocene epoch.)

8) scientific names of phyla, orders, classes, families, and genera, but not of species or subspecific taxa except where permitted by the botanical code (*see* p. 67)

9) complete vernacular or common names of species (but not subspecies) of birds in accordance with the check-list of the American Ornithologists' Union (1957) (*see* p. 70)

10) common names of insects *only* when in accordance with the list approved by the Entomological Society of America (*see* p. 70)

11) names of stars and other astronomical bodies (Earth, moon, and sun need not be capitalized except when they are used in a paper containing other astronomical terms.)

12) trade-marked names; do not use adjectives derived from trade names

13) the first word after a colon if the following words form a complete independent clause that is not logically dependent on the preceding clause

BOLDFACE
(marked by wavy underlining)

Mark for boldface:

1) names of genera, species, and subspecific taxa proposed for the first time
2) vectors in mathematics
3) volume numbers in literature citations

Printers' Measurements and Sizes of Type

Printers' measurements are based on the *point* (= 0.01384 inch). A *pica* is 12 points; there are about 72 points or 6 picas to an inch. Size of paper, engravings, trim size of page, and margins are usually expressed in inches; length of type line and width and depth of columns are expressed in picas; size of type and leads and the thickness of rules and spaces are expressed in points. The size of any font of type includes the height of ascenders (*d, f*) or capital letters, and the depth of descenders (*j, q*). The approximate English and metric equivalents of the various units are as follows:

1 inch	= 6	picas	= 72	points	= 25.4	mm
1 pica	= 12	points	= 1/6	inch	= 4.2	mm
1 point	= 1/72	inch	= 1/12	pica	= 0.35	mm

The *em* is a square of the body height of any size of type. A 1-em dash (—) in a 10-point type is 10 points long (length of the capital M in that font). One em is equal in length to 2 ens. Paragraphs are usually indented 1 em.

Rules (———) used in print have their thickness expressed in points and their length in picas. The one shown is 1-point, 2 picas.

Leaders (. . . .) have their length expressed in ems and size controlled by the specific type used.

Standard type is available in many sizes. Most articles in scientific journals are set in 8- or 10-point type, usually with 1- or 2-point leading (space) between printed lines. This paragraph is set in 10-point type with 2-point leading.

This sentence is set in lower case 6-point roman type

These are CAPITALS and SMALL CAPITALS in 8-point type

This is *italic* and **boldface** in 10-point type

This line is set in 12-point type

This line is set in 18-point type

The text of this manual is set in 10 point, the first headings in 24 point, and the tables in 8 or 6 point.

Casting Off   Casting off is a method for determining the number of column inches that will be occupied by a particular typescript when set in type of a certain size. On an ordinary typewriter every character is of the same width. In contrast, letters in printers' types are of many widths: capitals are wider than lower case letters, the *w* and *m* are wider than *e* and *h*, and the *i* and *l* are narrower, but these differences tend to average out. Printers can provide estimates of the number of characters per pica for any size of any font. For example, Caledonia type sets 3.14 characters per pica (in 8 point), 2.63 (in 10 point), or 2.26 (in 12 point). A simple formula for computing the number of printed pages from any manuscript is this:

No. of printed pages =

$$\frac{(\text{No. MS lines per page}) \times (\text{Characters and spaces per MS line}) \times (\text{No. of MS pages})}{(\text{Characters and spaces per printed line}) \times (\text{No. lines per printed page})}$$

6. Proof

The galley proofs are usually the only proofs the author sees. Few journals submit page proofs after correction of the galleys. Thus the galley proofs are the first indication of how the author's paper will appear. Remember that these are imprints on cheap paper, made on a hand press, with no breaks between pages; they may contain queries and symbols. The impressions on galley proofs are never as clear as those of the final printing.

Never cut the proof sheets; never obliterate the coded marks at the top—they identify the typesetter, location of type, and other essentials, and will be removed later. Never erase or eradicate marks on the proof; if an indicated change is not desired, cross it out and mark *stet* or *OK as set* beside it, and underline with dots the words to be retained.

Galley proofs are marked by the printer or the editor with various corrections, changes, and queries to the author. Answer each query (indicated by question mark). Avoid using an ambiguous *OK* in answer to a query. If you want the material to remain as set, cross out the question mark. In resetting the type from corrected galley proofs, the compositor scans the margins and resets only those lines marked for change. Make all corrections neatly and clearly in the margins, horizontally opposite the lines to which they apply. Type insertions of more than one line and attach them to the galley proof at the point where they should be made. *All* changes must be on the galley proofs, not in an accompanying letter. The typesetter has no means of following an extra set of instructions, nor does he have the time or inclination to run through the author's reasons for changes.

Check the proof, word for word, against the typescript, preferably with another person, and reading aloud. Verify all unusual names, all numerical data, bibliographic references, and the like against original sources. Check all divisions of words at the ends of lines. Even experienced typesetters may make errors, especially in uncommon scientific terms. Do not issue blanket orders, such as "set *Rosa* in italics throughout." Indicate each change individually. In marking proofs, use different colors from marks already there. It is customary for authors to mark printer's errors in red, author's alterations in blue or black. Indicate the position of figures and tables by a marginal notation, with a circle around it; also encircle all notes and instructions not to be set in type.

Proofreaders' Marks   Learn and use the customary proofreaders' marks (Fig. 3).

FIG. 3. *Proofreaders' marks*

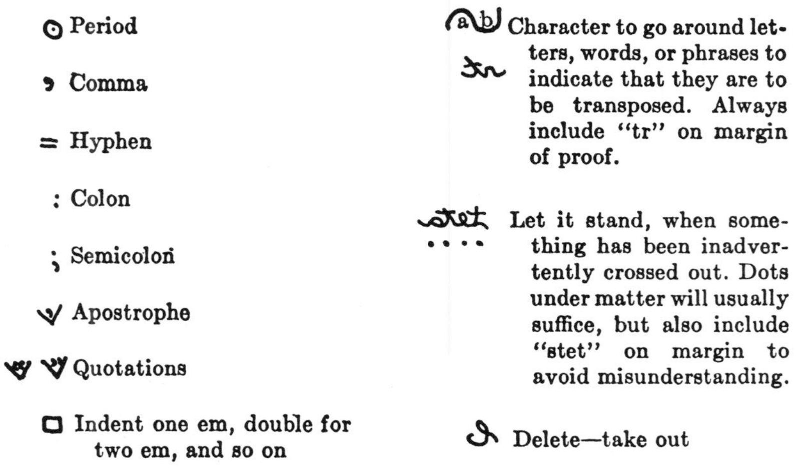

⊙ Period

❟ Comma

⸗ Hyphen

: Colon

; Semicolon

⩒ Apostrophe

⩔ ⩒ Quotations

☐ Indent one em, double for two em, and so on

⌒⌒ Character to go around letters, words, or phrases to indicate that they are to be transposed. Always include "tr" on margin of proof.

stet Let it stand, when something has been inadvertently crossed out. Dots under matter will usually suffice, but also include "stet" on margin to avoid misunderstanding.

𝓭 Delete—take out

Proofreaders' Marks
(Continued)

⊥ᵐ	One em dash
ℓ‖m	Two em parallel dash
⊥	Push down lead or space
⊂	Close up
/	Less space
∧	Caret—something to be inserted
⊘	Turn letter or line
#	Insert space
[or]	Move to left or to right
⊓ or ⊔	Move up or move **down**
( )	Parentheses
[ ]	Brackets
ᵗᵣ	Transpose
out o.c.	Out, see copy (be sure manuscript is returned if this is used)

✗	Broken letters or defective type
¶	Paragraph
no ¶	No paragraph
wf	Wrong font
✓✓✓	Equalize spacing
≡	Capitals and caps
=	Small capitals and sm. cap
lc.	Lower case
ᵇ/ₐ	Superior or inferior letters or figures
___	Italics, and ital
rom	Roman
spell	Spell out, if figure
②	Circle around figures means spell out
～～	Boldface bf

Correction requires two marks on the proof—one in the margin indicating what is to be done and another within the type indicating by a short perpendicular line or a caret (∧) the exact place where the change is to be made. If several corrections occur in one line, mark them from left to right and separate them by a long slant line (/) in the nearest margin.

Galley proof is not the place for extensive changes. If material must be added, insert it at the end of a paragraph or as a new paragraph. But an account of discoveries or observations made after the original manuscript was submitted must not be added this way. It is not ethical. Such matter belongs

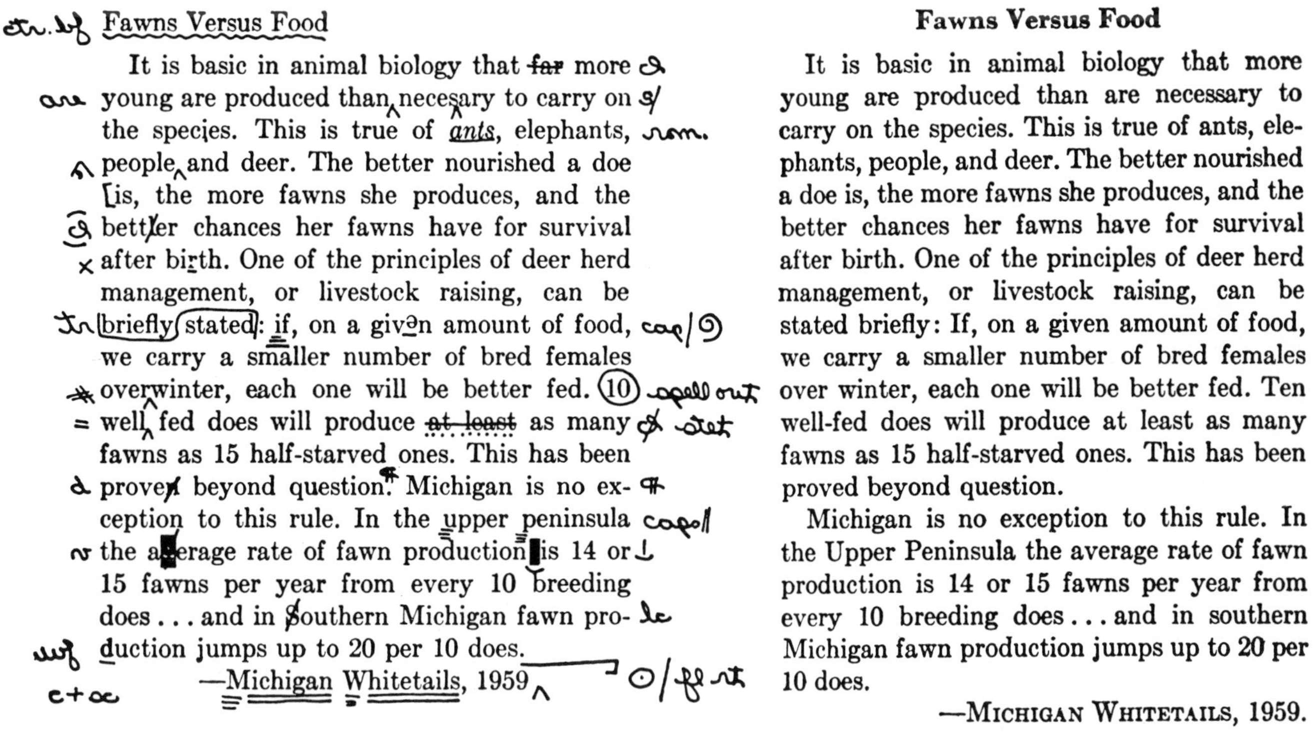

Fawns Versus Food

It is basic in animal biology that more young are produced than are necessary to carry on the species. This is true of ants, elephants, people, and deer. The better nourished a doe is, the more fawns she produces, and the better chances her fawns have for survival after birth. One of the principles of deer herd management, or livestock raising, can be stated briefly: If, on a given amount of food, we carry a smaller number of bred females over winter, each one will be better fed. Ten well-fed does will produce at least as many fawns as 15 half-starved ones. This has been proved beyond question.

Michigan is no exception to this rule. In the Upper Peninsula the average rate of fawn production is 14 or 15 fawns per year from every 10 breeding does . . . and in southern Michigan fawn production jumps up to 20 per 10 does.

—MICHIGAN WHITETAILS, 1959.

Fawns Versus Food

It is basic in animal biology that for more young are produced than necessary to carry on of the species. This is true of ants, elephants, people, and deer. The better nourished a doe [is, the more fawns she produces, and the better chances her fawns have for survival after birth. One of the principles of deer herd management, or livestock raising, can be briefly stated: if, on a given amount of food, we carry a smaller number of bred females over winter, each one will be better fed. Ten well fed does will produce at least as many fawns as 15 half-starved ones. This has been proved beyond question. Michigan is no exception to this rule. In the upper peninsula the average rate of fawn production is 14 or 15 fawns per year from every 10 breeding does . . . and in Southern Michigan fawn production jumps up to 20 per 10 does.

—Michigan Whitetails, 1959.

FIG. 4. *Portion of corrected galley proof*

in an addendum and requires the permission of the editor for inclusion. Insertions within a paragraph should, if possible, equal the deleted material letter for letter.

Figure 4 is a sample set in type (with more than the usual number of corrections) showing the necessary proofreaders' marks.

Nothing whatsoever should be added to or deleted from the original typescript. Return the typescript with the proofs.

Alterations Once type is set, changes are far more costly than the original typesetting. Much text matter is set on linotype machines, i.e., an entire line is cast as one "slug"; any change requires resetting the entire line and inserting it by hand. The addition of even one word to a line may necessitate resetting the rest of the paragraph.

Printer's errors are corrected at no cost to the author. The original manuscript, as marked for the printer by the editor, is the authority for identifying printer's errors and author's corrections. Printers and editors are grateful when authors clearly identify changes from the original copy. The cost of alterations beyond a certain minimum is usually charged to the author. Since compositors are well paid, it behooves the author to submit letter-perfect manuscript.

Illustrations Proofs of halftones on galley paper show much less detail and contrast than the finished product. Judge halftones by engraver's proofs. Corrections should be indicated in the margin and the engraver's proofs returned. Line cuts with minor faults may sometimes be repaired by the engraver. Usually, if the original art work was satisfactory, corrections are unnecessary and the originals need not be returned.

Identification of each figure should be marked on the proofs. If there is the slightest possibility of confusion, indicate the *top* edge of the proof. Check the stated magnification of illustrations.

Handling of Proof for Foreign Authors

To reduce postal expense, foreign authors too often submit manuscripts typed on onionskin paper, single-spaced, with scanty margins. Such manuscripts are unacceptable. As nearly as possible all manuscripts, whether domestic or foreign, are treated the same. Air mail is recommended for all transactions between editors and foreign authors. A foreign author often has some American colleague act for him with respect to minor editorial changes, rewrites, proofreading, and ordering of reprints.

7. Preservation of Materials for the History of Science

The preservation of original manuscripts, letters, and records is extremely important in the history of science. Such materials aid historians in their analyses of how scientific ideas develop, and how science influences the civilization it is helping to mold.

The Conference on Scientific Manuscripts held in 1960 suggested many worthwhile ways for the preservation of private papers and manuscripts of distinguished scientists. Such materials should be stored in archives of universities, historical societies, or other institutions. Editors of scientific journals and memoirs should follow the rule "that every official obituary or memoir include a statement regarding the location and condition of the private papers of the scientist concerned."

8. Indexing

An index is one of the most important means for retrieving scientific information. Scientific papers rarely have a separate index, but journals, books, and other documentary materials should have good indexes.

Authors may prepare indexes, but generally either the editor or an experienced indexer does this. Rules and instructions for making an index are given in references cited and in the Final Report (October 1963) of Z39 Subcommittee on Indexing, American Standards Association.

A few important suggestions are as follows:

1) Make the index promptly from page proof. Index all material in the introduction, main text, footnotes, and addenda.
2) Mark on the proof key words and names, significant phrases, and ideas or hypotheses. Key words are nouns or substantive phrases, not adjectives. Copy these items on filing cards, one entry to a card, or on perforated cards or paper. Arrange the items in alphabetical order, and then sort them into main headings and subheadings, making sure that each refers properly to the main subject, for example:

Ant(s), red, diseases of, 1, 10
Blackberry, effect of temperature on storage of, 2
Cold frames, plastic covers for, 8, 9, 10

DeForest, Lee, 100
Energy, derived from carbohydrates, 7
Feline pneumonitis virus, review of, 4

3) Capitalize initial words of main headings. In complex indexes, capitals and small capitals, italics, and boldface may be used to distinguish entries.

4) In multiple-word headings, use the word-by-word method of alphabetizing (New York before Newark) rather than the letter-by-letter method. File entries having the same name alphabetically (New York City, -Port, -State).

5) File hyphenated entries as if they were separate words.

6) File abbreviations as if they were spelled out.

7) File numbers as if spelled out, except that historical periods (17th century, 18th century) are filed chronologically. Numbers, Greek letters (α, β, γ), *ortho-, meta-, para-, sec-, tert-, d-, l-,* D-, L-, etc., used in chemical nomenclature are not alphabetized, except when establishing position under a heading.

8) Use a comma between each heading and the page number following and within a heading to indicate inverted order. Dashes may be used in place of headings or subheadings when the entry is repeated often.

9) Cross-reference the index to as many headings as desirable. Use a cross reference (*see*) from an entry to a synonymous term, and (*see also*) from an entry to another on a related subject. File *see also* references alphabetically before all other entries under a heading; if of minor significance, file under subheading or omit.

9. Useful References

Besides an up-to-date dictionary (*Webster's Third New International Dictionary*), an author or editor may get help from a variety of reference works. A few authoritative and generally useful books and articles are as follows:

Andrews, E. 1947. A history of scientific English. The story of its evolution based on a study of biomedical terminology. Richard R. Smith, New York. 342 p.

Baker, Sheridan. 1962. The practical stylist. Thos. Y. Crowell Co., New York.

Barzun, J., and H. F. Graff. 1962. The modern researcher. Harcourt Brace and World, New York. 306 p.

Brown, R. W. 1954. Composition of scientific words. Published by the author, U. S. Geological Survey, Washington. 882 p.

Crouch, W. G., and R. L. Zetler. 1954. A guide to technical writing. 2nd ed. Ronald Press Co., New York. 441 p.

Ferguson, C. W. 1959. Say it with words. Alfred A. Knopf, New York. 214 p.

Fishbein, M. 1957. Medical writing—the technic and the art. 3rd ed. Blakiston Division, McGraw-Hill Book Co., New York. 262 p.

Fowler, H. W. 1950. A dictionary of modern English usage. Oxford Univ. Press, London. 742 p.

Gensler, W. J., and K. D. Gensler. 1961. Writing guide for chemists. McGraw-Hill Book Co., New York. 149 p.

Gilman, W. 1961. The language of science. Harcourt, Brace & World, Inc., New York. 248 p.

Hewitt, Richard M. 1957. The physician-writer's book ... tricks of the trade of medical writing. W. B. Saunders Co., Philadelphia. 415 p.

Jaeger, E. C. 1955. A source-book of biological names and terms. 3rd ed. C. C Thomas, Springfield, Illinois. 317 p.

McAtee, W. L. 1940. On scholarly writing and critical reviewing. Sci. Monthly **51**:77–79.

McCartney, E. S. 1953. Recurrent maladies in scholarly writing. Univ. Michigan Press, Ann Arbor. 141 p.

Melcher, Daniel, and Nancy Larrick. 1956. Printing and promotion handbook: how to plan, produce, and use printing, advertising and direct mail. 2nd ed. McGraw-Hill Book Co., New York. 438 p.

Menzel, Donald H., Howard Mumford Jones, and Lyle G. Boyd. 1961. Writing a technical paper. McGraw-Hill Book Co., New York. 132 p.

Miles, S. R. 1957. How to make tables of information. Purdue Univ. Agr. Exp. Sta., Lafayette, Indiana. 86 p.

Ridgway, J. L. 1938. Scientific illustration. Stanford Univ. Press, Stanford, California. 173 p.

Roget, Peter Mark. 1933. Thesaurus of English words and phrases. Rev. ed. Grosset and Dunlap, New York. 705 p.

Skillin, Marjorie E., Robert M. Gay, and other authorities. 1948. Words into type: a guide in the preparation of manuscripts; for writers, editors, proofreaders and printers. Appleton-Century-Crofts, Inc., New York. 585 p.

Stiles, C. W. 1928. What constitutes publication? Science **67**:471–478.

Strunk, W., Jr., and E. B. White. 1959. The elements of style. Macmillan Co., New York. 71 p.

Trelease, S. F. 1958. How to write scientific and technical papers. Williams & Wilkins Co., Baltimore.

University of Chicago Press. 1949. A manual of style: containing typographical and other rules for authors, printers, and publishers recommended by the University of Chicago Press. Univ. Chicago Press, Chicago. 522 p.

U. S. Government Printing Office. 1959. U. S. Government Printing Office style manual. Rev. ed. U. S. Govt. Printing Office, Washington, D. C. 492 p.

Zweifel, Frances W. 1960. A handbook of biological illustration. Phoenix Science Series, Univ. Chicago Press.

Literature Cited in this Manual

American Ornithologists' Union. 1957. Check-list of North American birds. 5th ed. American Ornithologists' Union. Ithaca, N.Y. 691 p.

American Standards Association. 1941. American standard abbreviations for scientific and engineering terms. Bull. Y1, Z10.1–1941. American Standards Association, New York.

American Standards Association. 1959. Illustrations for publication and projection. Bull. Y15.1–1959. American Standards Association, New York.

American Standards Association. 1964. American Standard for periodical title abbreviations Z39.5. American Standards Association, New York.

Bailey, N. T. J. 1959. Statistical methods in biology. English Univ. Press, London, and John Wiley & Sons, Inc., New York. 200 p.

Baker, S. 1956. Scholarly style, or the lack thereof. Amer. Ass. Univ. Professors Bull. 42:464–470.

Bancroft, H. 1959. Introduction to biostatistics. Paul B. Hoeber of Harper & Brothers, New York. 210 p.

Breed, R. S., E. G. D. Murray, and N. R. Smith. 1957. Bergey's manual of determinative bacteriology. 7th ed. Williams & Wilkins Co., Baltimore. 1094 p.

Bryant, Margaret S. 1951. Bibliographic style. U.S. Dep. Agr. Bibliogr. Bull. 16. 30 p.

Buchanan, R. E. (*Chairman*), S. T. Cowan (*Sec.*), T. Wiken (*Sec.*), and W. A. Clark (*Sec.*), Editorial Board. 1958. International code of nomenclature of bacteria and viruses. Iowa State College Press, Ames. 186 p.

Chemical Abstracts Service. 1961. Chemical Abstracts list of periodicals with key to library files. American Chemical Society, Washington, D. C. 397 p.

Cockrum, E. Lendell. 1957. Laboratory manual of mammalogy. Burgess Publishing Co., Minneapolis, Minn. 160 p.

Entomological Society of America, Committee on Common Names of Insects (Jean L. Laffoon, *Chairman*) 1960, 1961. Common names of insects approved by the Entomological Society of America. Bull. Entomol. Soc. Amer. 6(4):175–211; 7(2):93.

Gove, Philip Babcock (*Ed.*). 1961. Webster's third new international dictionary of the English language unabridged. G. & C. Merriam Company, Springfield, Massachusetts.

History of Science Society. 1962. The conference on science manuscripts. ISIS 53(1):1–57.

International Committee of Anatomical Nomenclature. 1961. *Nomina Anatomica,* 2nd ed. Excerpta Medica Foundation, Amsterdam.

International Committee on Weights and Measures. 1962. (Comité International des Poids et Mesures.) Procès-Verbaux des Seances, 2e Série, Tome 28 (49e Session, 1960). Gauthier-Villars et Cie., Paris.

International Trust for Zoological Nomenclature. 1958. Official list of generic names in zoology, 1958; Part 1; names 1–1274. Official list of family-group names in zoology, 1958; Part 1; names 1–236. International Zoological Trust, London.

Kesling, R. V. 1958. Crimes in scientific writing. Turtox News 36:274–276.

Lanjouw, J. (*Chief Ed.*), and F. A. Stafleu (*Sec.*), Editorial Committee. 1956. International code of botanical nomenclature. Kemink en Zoon, Utrecht. 338 p.

Lawrence, G. H. M. 1951. Taxonomy of vascular plants. Macmillan Co., New York. 823 p.

Metcalf, Z. P. 1954. The construction of keys. Syst. Zool. 3:38–45; Fig. 1–6.

Riker, A. J. 1946. The preparation of manuscripts for Phytopathology. Phytopathology 36:953–977.

Schenck, E. T., and J. H. McMasters. 1956. Procedure in taxonomy. 3rd ed. Stanford Univ. Press, Stanford, California. 119 p.

Stoll, N. R. (*Chairman*), R. Ph. Dollfus, J. Forest, N. D. Riley, C. W. Sarbosky, C. W. Wright, R. V. Melville (*Sec.*), Editorial Committee, International Commission on Zoological Nomenclature. 1961. International code of zoological nomenclature. International Trust for Zoological Nomenclature, London. 176 p.

Union list of serials in libraries of the United States and Canada. 1943. H. W. Wilson Co., New York.

U. S. Government Printing Office. 1959. U. S. Government Printing Office style manual. Rev. ed. Washington, D.C. 492 p.

Vilmorin, R. de (*Chairman*), Editorial Committee of International Commission for Nomenclature of Cultivated Plants (IUBS). 1958. International code of nomenclature for cultivated plants. Regnum Vegetabile 10:1–28. Utrecht.

Wolf, F. A., and F. T. Wolf. 1947. The fungi. Vol. I, p. 163. John Wiley & Sons, New York.

Index